THE BEST
OF 'OLYMPIA'

For further information on The Olympia Press Traveller's
Companion Series and for a complete list of publications write to
The Olympia Press, 7 rue Saint-Séverin, Paris 5.

EDITED BY
MAURICE GIRODIAS

THE BEST
OF 'OLYMPIA'

AN ANTHOLOGY OF TALES, POEMS, SCIENTIFIC
DOCUMENTS AND TRICKS WHICH APPEARED IN THE
SHORT-LIVED AND MUCH LAMENTED
OLYMPIA MAGAZINE

No. 107

THE OLYMPIA PRESS
TRAVELLER'S COMPANION SERIES
GENERAL EDITOR : MAURICE GIRODIAS
PUBLISHED BY THE NEW ENGLISH LIBRARY LIMITED

PUBLISHED BY THE NEW ENGLISH LIBRARY LIMITED
FROM BARNARD'S INN, HOLBORN, LONDON, E.C.1.

*

© copyright by The Olympia Press, Paris, 1961, 1962, 1963
This anthology © copyright by The Olympia Press, Paris, 1966

*

First published in Great Britain
by The New English Library Limited in October 1966

Made and printed in Great Britain by
Waterlow & Son Ltd., London & Dunstable

CONTENTS

PREFACE

When I began publishing 'Olympia' in 1961 my idea was to create a house organ of a kind, and its function was mainly to attract and help in the discovery of new talent. But I was working against insuperable odds, and each issue of 'Olympia' marked an important date in my struggle against fate. In fact only four issues of that so-called monthly were printed between 1961 and 1963, and each one was at the cost of Herculean efforts.

Everything, I must confess, was going very badly during those years, and I was reaping the harvest of too much seed sown in too many directions. I think I owe an apology to all my friends for the trouble I caused them during that era of chaos.

A literary magazine is, in itself, one of the most doubtful ventures imaginable. How many have been conceived in a burst of enthusiasm which never reached their third issue? Co-editorship turns the best of friends into mortal enemies. The loftiest poet becomes a quivering mass of vanity when the time comes to turn his unpublished dreams into print. What appears to be a treasure of originality in manuscript form suddenly reveals itself as most commonplace and *déjà vu* when displayed on the printed page. Then, of course, there are all the material details, as complex and numerous as if one was running a ten million dollar business: the undelivered paper, the unpaid printer whose ink somehow never dries, the binder who either goes bankrupt or closes for summer holidays on the eve of delivery, the elusive subscribers, the world-weary bookseller who compliments one on one's faith and courage with pointed irony, and the forever unsatisfied contributors, who used to be one's friends and supporters before it all started, and who now rave, urge, protest, criticise, deride, denounce and generally do their best to hurt one in every possible way with an unlimited volume of spite and malevolence.

But those are only the classic problems and 'Olympia' had many other and more original odds against it. When I decided to publish that magazine I had already been the pet victim of the French censors for five or six years—although I was only publishing books in English, which they could not read. Years earlier my original edition of "Lolita", of "The Ginger Man", of "The Story of O", "Fanny Hill", of "Our Lady of the Flowers" and of "Candy" had been banned among dozens of other books of varying importance. I had bravely counter-attacked my censors in the Paris courts, and I had even won encouraging victories in the early stages; but after 1958 no hope was left to justify my resistance. The last judgments issued by the highest court in France, the *Conseil d'Etat,* made it quite clear: I was a bum, I had no business making things difficult for the French police who were only doing their duty; and people like me were a disgrace, in any case, and I was giving a bad name to France, to *le rayonnement de la culture française à l'étranger,* and all that.

Still I did not anticipate that strange wave of Gallic puritanism to hit such a dedicated enterprise as 'Olympia' Magazine. How wrong I was! Three days after the first issue had been released, the magazine was banned forever: by which I mean that the ban did not apply only to that first issue but to any subsequent issues I might decide to publish. I could still sell the magazine abroad, but one of the consequences of the ban was to deprive me of mailing privileges and other rights normally granted to periodicals.

Naturally I wrote to the Minister of the Interior, Monsieur Frey, to protest against what seemed to be an error. No answer. Then I went to see an official of that ministry, who acts as adviser in matters involving the Press and publishers. He listened to me with an expression of complacent boredom, and when I asked him whether he thought *le Ministre* would perchance suppress the ban, he simply answered that he did not think he would. I was beginning to lose patience, and I asked if he personally thought that such a ban was fair and whether it was not a rather unseemly restriction against freedom of the Press. He merely smiled, absently, as if he was thinking of something else of more substantial importance, such as the menu of his last meal. I got quite angry and asked with a shaking voice if the magazine had not been banned simply because I was its publisher. And at last I got his attention: "But of course, *cher Monsieur,*" he exclaimed with unfeigned joviality, "*c'est évident!* You know very well that you are not well noted by this administration, so you should not be surprised if your magazine has been suppressed as a matter of routine. And now if you will allow me . . ." he concluded, half getting-up and showing me the door with a perfunctory flourish.

I was floored. Was this France? Salazar's officials were more scrupulous, less presumptuous! But perhaps I had been a fool not to understand what was happening to my country: it was so obvious! Already, in 1946, I had been the first target of the new censorship when I had brought out the French version of Miller's "Tropic of Capricorn". I had been sued, along with two other publishers, and *"l'affaire Miller"* was the first serious case of literary censorship to take place in France—under a socialist regime!—since the prosecutions against Baudelaire and Flaubert, nearly one century earlier.

I was still mulling over those dark thoughts when I entered my office. On my desk was a summons from a magistrate: I was being indicted for having published, in the first issue of 'Olympia' Magazine, excerpts from two books previously banned by the French administration—"Candy" and "The Woman Thing". Should I go on with this dire story? If I do, no doubt Mr. George Steiner will write somewhere that "I tend to whine," and perhaps, for once, he will be right. .

Well, on top of the ban, I was sentenced by the lower courts to a stiff sentence, which was confirmed by the Court of Appeals. I appealed against that decision once more, as was my right, to the higher jurisdiction, the *Cour de Cassation*; and forgot about the case until my lawyer informed me that I had won a half-victory: the *Cour de Cassation* had cancelled the previous judgment and, in keeping with the rule set up by Napoleon, I was to be tried again by a provincial Court of Appeals a few months later.

On the eve of the appointed day, for some obscure reason, I had too much to drink and when I met my friend and lawyer, Leo Matarasso, at the station I had a splitting headache. I could hardly see, my speech was blurred and incoherent, and none of the medication he forced on me during the two-hour train ride had any effect on my hangover.

We looked for the courthouse, Leo half supporting me with one arm while carrying his *avocat's* robes under the other, and we finally stumbled to the front of a great romantic building in the eighteenth century style, which was graced by a monumental stone staircase covered with moss and weeds. That image of abandon brought to mind poems by Novalis or *Le Grand Meaulnes,* with visions of dead loves and hopeless pursuits. I was beginning to cry silently when Leo tugged me by the sleeve saying that it seemed to be a mistake all right, but that we were going to see if we could find some human being inside, and ask where the real courthouse was. A door was open in the east wing. Inside, a crepuscular light half revealed walls covered with century-old legal posters; the floor was strewn with masses of ancient files lying under a thick blanket of dust. From far away we heard a creaking and uneven noise: a man was coming towards us, pushing a wheelbarrow loaded with refuse. Leo asked for the courthouse; the man silently pointed to a staircase and then disappeared into the shadows.

Two floors up, three doors to open, and we found ourselves in a gigantic hall, apparently taking up the entire width of the centre part of the building; freshly painted walls, outsized statues shining white, immensely tall windows and doors; and no one in sight. But obviously the old courthouse was being redecorated, and all we had to do now was to find the right courtroom. We opened a door at random, and gasped. It looked like a courtroom, but a courtroom for Zeus himself, certainly not for mortal justice. Everything was outsized, and brand new. At the far end an immense and majestic podium covered with a dark green carpet held a long table of unusual height, hidden under heavy drapes of the same hue. Three gigantic thrones, the middle one higher than the others, increased the impression of awsome majesty; their design was curvaceous, but any frivolous implications such shapes might have carried were smothered under the thick protection of bottle-green plush. To the right and to the left, armchairs of more reasonable proportions flanked the central edifice, and, placed at a lower level on each side of the tribunal were the green-draped pulpits of the public prosecutor and the court clerk. Facing the podium, at a respectful distance, were the lawyers' benches, of an unusually handsome design. Far away, at the back and on the sides, were the benches reserved for the public. The walls and the large square pillars were painted in white, but their base, up to eye level, was decorated in dark green imitation marble. I noticed that an iron ring hanging from one of the walls, presumably a leftover from earlier days, had also been painstakingly painted in imitation marble.

We tiptoed inside, not daring to speak. Suddenly Leo pressed my arm: I looked in the direction of his stare and stifled an exclamation of surprise. A ray of sunlight was falling from one of the tall windows and revealed a strange figure: a man dressed in long, black, monacal robes was standing there, totally immobile, his colourless, emaciated face and skull completely shaven, with the unblinking stare of a hermit painted by El Greco.

This was a little too eerie for me and I vaguely sensed that Leo himself, a staunch champion of logic and the Cartesian approach, felt his reason vacillate. He whispered something, made me sit on a bench, and walked hurriedly to the door half-hidden behind the tribunal. I was beginning to doze off when he came back with a large

ix

grin on his face. I woke up completely: the man in black had disappeared. Leo explained that he was nothing more than a minor court official, whose function was to carry papers around, and that he was quite old and slightly out of his mind so he had been permitted as a special favour to wear that strange mediaeval costume. No harm in that. Leo chuckled; then he looked worried again. He said: "Listen, I have just seen the judge and his two assessors. He does not look like a bad judge as judges go, but . . . *Enfin,* I must ask you to be very quiet and very polite when you see him. You are in no condition to make speeches anyway. All you have to do when they come in and call for you is walk to the bar over there, on the floor, answer yes or no, look contrite and that's all. Leave the rest to me. *You understand?"*

I shook my head. I understood—obscurely. But why was Leo so worried? What was the matter with my judge? I was still hazily puzzling over those questions when the man in black re-entered the room, walked to the middle of the floor and facing an imaginary public, intoned the usual inaugural phrase in a creaky voice: *"Messieurs, la Cour."*

Two or three lawyers in funny, outmoded provincial robes and bonnets, and an awe-struck peasant family then revealed their presence by getting to their feet. I stood up with difficulty, but nearly fell to the floor in hysterics when the door opened for the hierarchic procession of court officials: the head judge was a dwarf. Or so small that the dimensions of the decor made him look like one. All the others behind him looked roughly normal but I thought that I detected an ill-concealed grin on their faces; a sick fantasy, no doubt, and I caught Leo's look of concern, pleading with me, silently, to keep cool, silent and in control of myself.

The judge sat down, the other members of the court sat down, the three members of the public and the four lawyers shuffled to their seats. All I could see of the judge now was the top half of his forehead. His assessors now looked slightly embarrassed and peevish. Then the judge cleared his throat; he spoke, and his voice was a tiny squeak like a little girl's voice would sound if she had a bad sore throat. I collapsed as if mortally stricken. Leo was looking at me again with desolate intensity, and that sobered me: all right, I would do my best. But it was a tough job. There was a long silence and the little voice spoke up again, calling my name.

I stood up, and staggered forward on the highly polished parquet floor in the direction of the bar, my right hand extended to grasp the thin rail which would safeguard my uncertain balance. The attorney-general was looking at me strangely. When I reached the bar, after what seemed an endless ordeal of slow motion, it lurched forward under my weight, to the left, then slowly back to the right, and I realized that the bar was held up by two thin sticks which had been only loosely fixed to the floor; someone had not had time to finish his job! And I was to inaugurate that bar! I felt great tears rolling down my face, whether of mirth or horror I did not know. I told myself: "I am certainly quite emotional today," and I sensed the attorney-general's gaze on me, and Leo's anguished stare on the back of my head.

I had just enough in me to answer a strangled yes or no between sobs, and I was told to return to my seat in a tone of voice in which I fancied I could detect a trace of pity.

x

Then the attorney-general stood up and spoke. I could not understand what he was saying, but I was able to study him; he was a youngish man, he would be zealous in his job as his ambition was obviously to be promoted to a Paris court. He was making gestures in my direction with his hands and chin, and I did not have to hear his words to know that he was fulminating against me in the name of Society, of Tradition, Family, Religion, Nation and so on. Legal arguments would have no place in his diatribe. And it did not matter a bit, what he said, not even to himself: he knew that perfectly well, and the others knew it, and they knew that I knew, or if I was too drunk or stupid to know, at least my *avocat* was supposed to know. It's all a game. And we've all a living to make.

Then it was Leo's turn. Leo also has a living to make but is more delicate about it, and has a sense of humour. He proved it in his choice of literary references; he read a page from the diary of *les frères Goncourt,* in the belief that that name would ring a bell in the memory of the magistrates, as they would undoubtedly have come across it in their newspapers in connection with the famous Goncourt Prize. He spoke well, slowly, stopping every time he saw one of the magistrates closing his eyes or looking out of the window. He spoke firmly, but respectfully, with humour, but simplicity. I found myself listening to him, and understanding everything he was saying. Wonderful! A real master at his job is Leo.

And so, also, thought the attorney-general! He was bristling with impatience, turning in his armchair, fingering papers nervously. Leo, his gaze shifting slowly from one of his opponents to the other, spoke of the old tradition of the courts, of culture, of the debt of society to its artists, of *La France, patrie des arts,* of the extraordinary occasion for such an enlightened court to show its moral courage and independence, when such a regrettable mistake had been made by a Paris Court of Appeal, already sanctioned by the *Cour de Cassation. . . .*

The attorney-general was shaking with uncontrollable emotion and he was now trying to interrupt Leo with his gestures, brandishing an open copy of 'Olympia' Magazine in his direction. Leo rounded up his speech and then sat down. I was mentally applauding; the magistrates seemed subdued. I had lost sight entirely of the judge's skull.

Then the attorney-general stood up again and begged permission to make one final remark. This was granted. He then asked the magistrates, now alert and watchful behind their high green wall, if anyone of them could read the English language. The answer was no. The attorney-general seemed to have expected as much. *"Eh, bien,"* he exclaimed, "with the Court's permission, I can read that language. Oh, certainly, I am no expert, but I know enough to judge the quality of this infamous publication. Literature! Pah!" he spat. "This is simply disgusting, no poetic inspiration, no redeeming qualities. Beatnik stories. Your Honour, look at this story, for instance, 'The Woman Thing'. You have these two young people, an American girl and a Scottish sculptor, who never works. They have been spending weeks on end in a bed, practically without going out. The sheets are complacently described as being in a revolting state. Then they talk, those two young foreigners, they exchange remarks, most of which do not seem to make any sense at all. And all of a sudden, do you know what the man tells the girl? I am sorry, Your Honour, I am most sorry if I have to wound your sensibilities, but you must know what is written . . . Naturally it will not be recorded . . . Well, the man," the attorney-general roared, "the man turns to the girl and says: 'Look at all that shit on the floor.'"

The dramatic gesture of the right hand indicated the floor of the entire courtroom. Treated thus, the metaphor became much too vivid. The magistrates winced. Leo closed his eyes. We had lost our case.

*   *   *

But here I am, whining again. It is not true that my experience with 'Olympia' Magazine was all bad. We did publish four issues, after all, in spite of the ban; and the fifth, which failed to come out, was to contain a wealth of wonderful material including some of the first published writings of Philip Fariña, who recently died, just a few days after his first published book came out.

The magazine helped me discover several writers I like and in whom I have great faith. It seemed somehow unfair to let all that material be lost in the hands of French censors and this small volume, however incoherent it may appear in style and design, will somewhat appease my remorse in that respect. The discovery of Jonathan Kozol, Jascha Kessler, and Stephen Schneck (recent winner of the Formentor Prize) will leave no one indifferent, I presume, and Claire Rabe's filters bear the hallmark of the highest magic art.

MAURICE GIRODIAS

New York
June, 1966

Girdle of chastity of French origin, XVIth century, with protective device in polished ivory, and steel waistband garnished with velvet *(Cluny Museum, Paris)*.

CHASTITY BELTS: A MYSTIFICATION?
by PROFESSOR HENRY CRANNACH

On Friday, July 7th, 1961, the famed Académie Française closed for the summer months; however, they devoted this last session to the subject of Chastity. They redefined the word as meaning "Etat de celui qui est chaste, qui s'abstient en amour de tout plaisir illicite. Mais signifie aussi entière abstinence des plaisirs."* Thus the term "ceinture de chasteté" (chastity belt) was introduced officially into the dictionary.

These devices were worn primarily among women although there has been documented mention of girdles of chastity that were carried on the

*"The state of those who are chaste, who abstain from love and all illicit pleasures, as well as signifying a total abstinence of pleasure."

bodies of young boys as well, during puberty. It is also rumoured that the prudent bee-master makes sure his Queen bee in overly ecstatic states is equipped with such a device.

The most favourable theory concerning the introduction of chastity belts into Western Europe is the one of the Crusaders who returning from the East brought with them a knowledge of oriental sexual customs, of which the girdle of chastity was distinctly one, and thereby found its way to Venice, the centre of oriental trade during mediæval times. Since there is little documentation on the actual *wearing* of chastity belts, those documents available discuss rather the sexual and social mores of the periods when the wearing of a girdle of chastity was supposedly applied than the girdle itself. There are singular evidences at a much later date, usually about jealous husbands who forced their wives to

13

wear chastity belts. These instances are known as they have become legal case histories. More truth lies in this motivation than in the common misconception of the Crusaders forcing their spouses to be so girdled until their return. The practice appears to have been enforced by jealous husbands who had no intention of going anywhere. Particularly during the thirteenth century the seat of voluptuousness was in itself a thing of value to be protected from outside violence and considered a sacred treasure. A woman's body belonged to her husband; Italian jealousy being notorious, the state of things in Italy was such that a girdle for protecting chaste virtues outside the marriage fitted well into the sexual mores.

Some of the German woodcuts dating from about 1590 depict the scene of the lady in question as seated at the foot of a large bed completely naked save for the heavy padlock securing a girdle of chastity around her lower body. She is shown handing a large key to a gentleman (her husband) standing before her while, hidden behind the curtains of her bed, the lover stands, holding the purse which will pay for the duplicate key. In the foreground a fool is trying to keep a swarm of insects in a basket and to the left a cat is watching a mouse.

Among the illustrations of Goya there are both mystifications and actual representations of people and animals wearing chastity belts. There is no proof that these objects were ever worn by women but there is a circumstance which led to the discovery of a famous girdle that bears repeating. This girdle was at Munich in the collection of Mr. Pachinger, who originally discovered it. Mr. E. J. Dingwall in his excellent study *The Girdle of Chastity* relates how Mr. Pachinger visited a little provincial town in upper Austria, in 1889, where restorations were being carried out on an old church which had been built towards the middle of the fifteenth century, and there encountered his discovery . . . "The slab had to be raised, revealing a cavity containing an ancient leaden coffin. They transferred the object to a corner of the churchyard and on examination it proved to be a leaden casket, about 1.80 m. long, its dark grey smooth surfaces showing neither inscriptions nor a coat of arms." Mr. Dingwall goes on to describe rotten wooden boards which crumbled away to disclose the skeleton below: a skull well preserved and upon it perched a richly braided coiffure-like wig. "The colour of the hair was reddish and under the rays of the sun it shone like gold. The splendid set of teeth

14

Model preserved in the Palazzo Ducale, Venice *(ph. Osvaldo Böhm).*

indicated that the deceased had been a young person, and the artistic mode of dressing the hair and also the fine raiment of silk that it was a woman of rank." After raising the skeleton from the crumbling boards only the front parts of her dress were preserved, showing a dark damask pattern appearing to be of a date some time after the beginning of the seventeenth century. This soon crumbled to dust when disturbed, revealing an apron-like linen shift and a remnant of a short petticoat. "Both of these were yellow brown in colour and partly mouldy, so that parts of the ribs and pelvic bones were exposed, and when the whole of the skeleton became visible it was seen that the pelvic bones were surrounded by an iron hoop, jointed in several pieces."

This chastity belt was dated as early seventeenth century with the frontal slit furnished on either side with twenty-one teeth. It would appear that the lady whose skeleton lay in the coffin was one of the less fortunate ones who even in her grave was burdened with the girdle of chastity. Mr. Dingwall would like us to believe that this is proof enough of ladies actually wearing chastity belts, but might not it have been that her master, out of love, wanted to guard his lady's chastity throughout eternity?

15

Bolognese model.

Swashbuckler (clamp spring shuts tight on any movement other than normal walking).

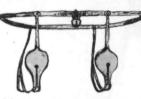

Model for Siamese twins (Siam).

Hermaphrodite (rare).

Singapore strangler.

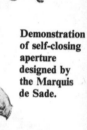

Demonstration of self-closing aperture designed by the Marquis de Sade.

Gay deceiver.

Windjammer.

Bolivian bloomers.

PURSEWARDEN'S INCORRIGIBILIA
by LAWRENCE DURRELL

It will be some time before the Pursewarden papers and manuscripts are definitively sorted and suitably edited; but a few of his *boutades* have turned up in the papers of his friends. Here are two examples of what someone called his "incorrigibilia"; he himself referred to them as **Authorised** Versions. The first, which was sung to the melody of *Deutschland, Deutschland Über Alles*, in a low nasal monotone, generally while he was shaving, went as follows:

(ph. Martha Rocher.)

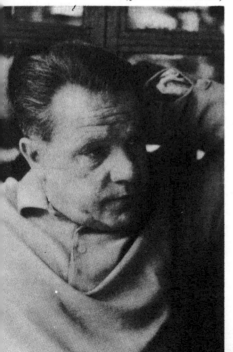

Take me back where sex is furtive
And the midnight copper roams;
Where instead of comfy brothels
We have Lady Maud's At Homes.
Pass me up that White Man's Burden
Fardels of Democracy;
Three faint cheers for early closing,
Hip-Hip-Hip Hypocrisy!
Sweet Philistia of my childhood
Where our valiant churchmen pant:
"Highest standard of unliving,
Longest five-day week of Cant."
Avert A.I.! Shun Vivisection!
Join the RSPCA,
Lead an anti-litter faction!
Leave your leavings in a tray!
Cable grandma I'll be ready,
Waiting on the bloody dock;
With a hansom for my luggage—
Will the French release my cock?
Take me back in An Appliance,
For I doubt if I can walk;
Back to art dressed in a jockstrap,
Back to a Third Programme Talk.
Roll me back down Piccadilly
Where our National Emblem stands,
Watching coppers copping tartlets,
Eros! wring thy ringless hands!
Ineffectual intellectual
Chewing of the Labour rag,
Take me back where every Cause
Is round the corner, in the bag.
Buy me then my steamer ticket
For the land for which I burn . . .
Yet, on second thoughts, best make it
The usual weekday cheap return!

DREAM MACHINE
by BRION GYSIN

"Had a transcendental storm of colour visions today in the bus going to Marseilles. We ran through a long avenue of trees and I closed my eyes against the setting sun. An overwhelming flood of intensely bright patterns in supernatural colours exploded behind my eyelids: a multi - dimensional kaleidoscope whirling out through space. I was swept out of time. I was out in a world of infinite number. The vision stopped abruptly as we left the trees. Was that a vision? What happened to me?"

That is an entry in my journal, dated December 21, 1958.

I found out exactly what had happened to me when, in 1960, William Burroughs gave me to read, *"The Living Brain,"* by Gray Walter. I learned that I had been subjected to flicker, not by a stroboscope, but by the sun whose light had been interrupted at a precise rate per second by the evenly spaced trees as I raced by. A many million-to-one chance. My experience utterly changed the subject and style of my painting. Walter in this connection makes the magnificent surmise: ". . . Perhaps, in a similar way, our arboreal cousins, struck by the setting sun in the midst of a jungle caper, may have fallen from perch to plain, sadder but wiser apes."

Ian Sommerville, who had also read Walter, wrote me from Cambridge on February 15, 1960: "I have made a simple flicker machine; a slotted cardboard cylinder which turns on a gramophone at 78 rpm with a light bulb inside. You look at it with your eyes shut and the flicker plays over your eyelids. Visions start with a kaleidoscope of colours on a plane in front of the eyes and gradually become more complex and beautiful, breaking like surf on a shore until whole patterns of colour are pounding to get in. After a while the visions were permanently behind my eyes and I was in the middle of a whole scene with limitless patterns being generated around me. There was an almost unbearable feeling of spatial movement for a while but it was well worth getting through for I found that when it stopped I was high above earth in a universal blaze of glory. Afterwards I found that my perception of the world around me had increased very notably. All conceptions of being dragged or tired had dropped away . . . ."

I made a "machine" from his ensuing description and added to it an interior cylinder covered with the type of painting I have developed in the three years since my first flicker experience. The result, eyes open or eyes closed, warranted taking out a patent, and on July 18, 1961 I received brevet no. P.V. 868,281 entitled: *"Procedure and apparatus for the production of artistic visual sensations."* The official description of the Dream Machine reads in part: "This invention, which has artistic and medical application, is remarkable in that perceptible results are obtained when one approaches one's eyes, either open or closed, to the outer cylinder slotted with regularly spaced openings revolving at a determined speed. These sensations may be modified by a change in speed, or by a change in the disposition of the slots, or by changing the colours and patterns on the interior of the cylinder . . ."

Flicker may prove to be a valid instrument of practical psychology: some people see and others do not. The Dream Machine, with its patterns visible to the open eye, induces people to see. The fluctuating elements of flickered design support the development of autonomous "movies," intensely pleasurable and, possibly, instructive to the viewer.

What is art? What is colour? What is vision? These old questions demand new answers when, in the light of the Dream Machine, one sees all of ancient and modern abstract art with eyes closed.

In the Dream Machine nothing would seem to be unique. Rather, the elements seen in endless repetition, looping out through numbers beyond number and back, show themselves to be thereby a part of the whole. This, surely, approaches the vision of which the mystics have spoken; suggesting as they did that it was a unique experience.

Art has been confounded with the art object—the stone, the canvas, the paint—and has been valued because, like the mystic experience, it was supposed to be unique. Marcel Duchamp was, no doubt, the first to recognise an element of the infinite in the *Ready-Made*—our industrial objects manufactured in "infinite" series. The Dream Machine may very well show you an eternal series of gas jets burning with an unearthly flame, but to dub an individual gas jet a "unique art object" by adding the artist's signature, is to make the elementary mistake of taking the merely tangible world for the visible world.

My first experience of natural flicker through the trees made me realize that the one and only thing which cannot be taken from the picture is light—everything else can be utterly transmuted or can go. The Dream Machine may bring about a change of consciousness inasmuch as it throws back the limits of the visible world and may, indeed, prove that there are no limits.

When I had seen some hundreds of hours of flicker, I thought of Gray Walter and his vision of the first mutated apes being knocked out of the trees in the primeval forest by the flicker of the sun through the branches, and I wrote:

"One Ready Ape hit the ground and the impact knocked a word out of him. Maybe he had an infected throat. He spoke. In the Word was his beginning. He looked about and saw the world differently. He was one changed ape. I look about now and see this world differently. Colours are brighter and more intense—traffic lights at night glow like immense jewels. The ape became a man. It must be possible to become something more than a man."

To Construct your own Dream Machine:

(A) Separate the two black panels from the body of the review: cut them off neatly so as to eliminate the white margin on the left. Cut off the white strips, in order to obtain two panels with no white showing at all, and with five windows in each.

(B) Make a cylinder by gluing the two panels end to end; the black and red design should appear inside, and the two panels should be attached together so that the ten windows will all be spaced evenly around the cylinder.

(C) Place the cylinder on a gramophone turn-table set to revolve at 78 rpm. Suspend an electric light bulb (100 watts) inside the cylinder, on level with the windows.

(D) Switch on the gramophone and bulb. Bring your eyes as close to the windows as possible. Stroboscopic patterns can be seen with the light playing on your *closed* eyelids. To use the machine with open eyes, the bulb should be placed so as not to remain visible. Effects seen with the eyes open sometimes take a minute or two to resolve.

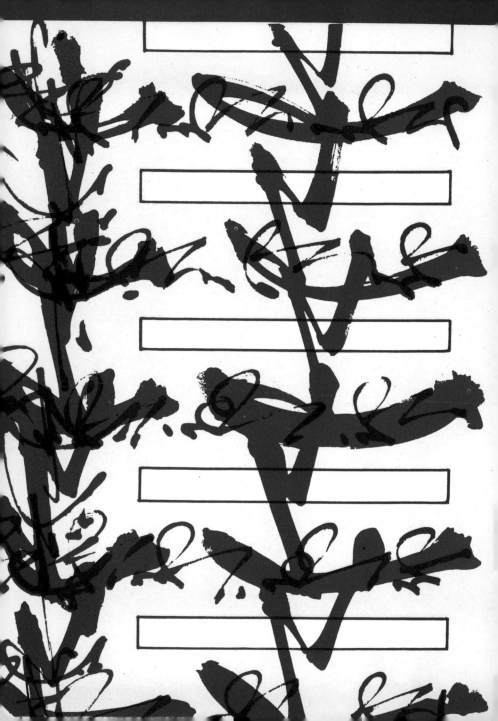

FLICKER
by IAN SOMMERVILLE

Brain waves, minute electrical oscillations associated with brain activity, can be measured accurately and graphically recorded by the electroencephalograph (EEG) machine. EEG records show that brain rhythms divide into groups according to frequency. One of these groups, the alpha or scanning rhythms, is strongest when the brain is unoccupied, searching for pattern; weakest during purposeful thinking, eyes open studying pattern. The strength and type of rhythms, vary between individuals. The EEG records of some primitive peoples are similar to those of a ten year old in our society. Variations occur with age. The alpha rhythms do not appear in children until they are about four years old.

Having obtained graphic records of brain waves, the next step was to see how these could be modified experimentally. Subjects were asked to visualize scenes, do mental arithmetic, etc. while their EEG record was being taken: minimal results were recorded until electric oscillations or light flashes were played on them. This flicker at precise rates per second produced radical change in the EEG graph and the subjects reported "dazzling lights of un-earthly brilliance and colour developing in magnitude and complexity of pattern as long as the stimulation lasted."

Similar effects may be produced on a small scale by pressure on the eyeball, rotating of the closed eye, close-viewing, dark-adaptation or blinking at the bright sky, sudden body movement, mechanical or psychical shock, chemicals, periodic light pulses produced by speeding through an avenue of trees with the sun behind them—"natural flicker."

The intense and even overwhelming effects of coloured pattern seen under stimulation must be distinguished from the "hallucinations" known in psychiatry, as well as from those visions which bring about permanent personality change. However, recorded mystic visions, perhaps due to a metabolic state as suggested by Aldous Huxley, often mention these same dazzling lights. St. Augustine wrote: "And thou didst beat back the infirmity of my own eyes, darting thy beams of light upon me most strongly and I trembled . . ." The most striking case of personality change is that of St. Paul who was journeying to Damascus in his chariot when, ". . . suddenly, there shined round about him a light from heaven. And he fell to earth . . ."

The elements of pattern which have been recorded by subjects under flicker show a clear affinity with the designs found in prehistoric rock-carving, painting, and idols of world-wide distribution: India, Czechoslovakia, Spain, Mexico, Norway and Ireland. They are found also in the arts of many primitive peoples of Australia, Melanesia, West Africa, South Africa, Central America and the Amazon. Children's drawings often spontaneously depict them, and in modern art (Klee, Miro, etc.) they are to be recognized in profusion.

A scientific group in Munich, using an electrode strapped to the forehead as stimulus, is attempting to catalogue such elementary subjective light patterns as their subjects report.

In England, Gray Walter works on the stimulation of brain rhythm responses to flashing light. He has used a stroboscope (an electronic flash generator) playing on closed eyes. The most marked effects occur when the stroboscope frequency is in tune with the subject's own alpha rhythm. The viewer sees counter-revolving Catherine-wheels, explosive fountains of unearthly brilliant colours, etc. The interesting point is that, independent as they are of a prominent part of the eye's mechanism—its shutter and lense—

these effects cover the entire visual field and are everywhere in focus. This is in sharp contrast to normal vision in which only a small centre portion of the visual field is in focus.

Flicker may play a part in cinematic experience. The frame speed of film is three to four times faster than the average alpha rhythm but the film viewed may include flicker frequences as a sub-harmonic. Films and TV impose external rhythms on the mind, altering the brain waves which are otherwise as individual as finger-prints. It is entirely possible that the EEG records of a generation of TV watchers will be similar, even identical—although differing from those which present research reveals.

Our ancestors saw the creatures of the constellations in the apparently unorganized distribution of the stars. It has been shown experimentally through the viewing of random white dots on a screen that man tends to find pattern and picture where objectively there is none: his mental process shapes what it sees. External resonators, such as flicker, tune in with our internal rhythms and lead to their extension.

The Dream Machine began as a simple means to investigate phenomena whose description excited our imaginations — our faculty of image-making which flicker was said to stimulate. The basic machine is that which anyone can put together from the instructions on p. . Maximum effect is achieved with a light of at least 100 watts when flicker plays over closed lids brought as close as possible to the cylinder revolving at 78 rpm. This may not produce everybody's exact alpha rhythm but the effects can be astonishing. They continue to develop over a long period of time. We offer you, if you care to follow the instruction, a first taste. More elaborate machines can be obtained.

Brion Gysin added an interior cylinder covered with the type of painting which he had developed from his first "natural flicker" experience, and with eyes open the patterns became externalized, seemed to catch on fire, and lick up from inside the whirling cylinder. In the bigger machines of his design whole moving pictures are produced and seem to be in flux in three dimensions on a brilliant screen directly in front of the eyes. Elaborate geometric constructions of incredible intricacy build up from bright mosaic into living fire-balls like the *mandalas* of Eastern mysticism surprised in their act of growth.

The intensity of the effect varies with the individual; melancholics tend to be irritated, some see nothing. The use of opiates and barbiturates would seem to seal off the patterns almost completely. Rhythmic sound, particularly Arab music and jazz, modulate the vision in which patterns keep time with the music.

FRANKIE AND JOHNNY
New Style

Livin' in a functional greenhouse
In tastefully painted tones,
Squattin' on chairs of tubular steel
And dicin' with the baby's bones.
    Chorus: He was her man, etc.

Goldfish swimming in a circle,
Swimming round and round like
    thoughts,
While a frigidaire keeps the bottle
    cold
And the drinks in their glass retorts.
    Chorus: *Ibid.*

Help us to bear all our follies
In a forest of sanitary bricks,
Where no bed-bug lives in the closet
And no death-watch beetle ticks.
    Chorus: *Ibid.*

With faces blanker than porcelain
In a forest of termite steel
Where the saxophones keep repeat-
    ing
"The People shall not feel."
    Chorus: *Ibid.*

Where the psyche fades like a violet
Overlooked in a dry box-wall;
We're rehearsing the Second Com-
    ing
Unaware of the Second Fall.
    Chorus: *Ibid.*

Riffle a book in the library,
Yawn at the clocks in the sky,
Rove the city streets with a brief-
    case,
Feeling your life go by.
    Chorus: *Ibid.*

Once the saints were good box-
    office
And the times seemed full of sap,
But things haven't been right since
    Eden.
Come here and sit in my lap.
    Chorus: *Ibid.*

It's the end of a city culture
And an end of the age of Sex,
Soon we'll multiply by fission
By courtesy of World Shell-Mex.
    Chorus: *Ibid.*

A kiss to the deathless Helen
An embrace to the Prodigal Son,
For the nerves are dying in their
    bodies
Horribly, one by one.
    Chorus: *Ibid.*

The taste buds die like mushrooms
And the sex buds die like spore
And this ain't no time to wake them
'Cause there ain't no Time no more.
    Chorus: *Ibid.*

There ain't no n-dimensions
To make a place for love
And there ain't no Space to fit it in

Below or up above.
    Chorus: *Ibid.*

Frankie and Johnny were lovers
But the Lord waxed mighty wroth
When he saw them trying to die
    together,
A-knitting their own winding-cloth.
    Chorus: *Ibid.*

For their race was the race of Adam,
Their mother was the golden Eve,
But they died in the XXth Century
Leaving nothing to believe.
    Chorus: *Ibid.*

THE TRIAL OF THE TEMPLARS
by ANN FEDERMAN

One of the most ancient methods of political warfare consists in denouncing publicly the moral character of the enemy, and then destroying him for the sake of orthodoxy. Captain Dreyfus and Roger Casement, Joan the Maid and Galileo belong to the hordes of imaginary deviationists who fell the victims of cynical lies and accusations.

In such conspiracies, the political and religious powers are often allied, the one lending its secular arm and the other its volumes of canon law. The major fault of the Templars was to own great riches, and their fall was provoked by the greed of King Philip of France; to give his plot some consistency, the King enlisted a Pope as accomplice, who covered the tortures and trumped up charges with the authority of the Church of Rome.

The trial of the Templars stands out as one of the most outrageous crimes ever committed in the name of God.

Res amara, flebilis, res quidem cogitatu horribilis, cogitatu terribilis . . . begins the warrant of arrest: "Bitter thing, to make one weep,

horrible to think, terrible to think" . . . holding the Order guilty of obscene and blasphemous rites whereby initiates of the Temple were to spit three times upon a crucifix and deny Christ, of having and obeying immoral secret statutes, of worshipping an idol and practising the grossest sodomical habits "which surpass the limits of debauchery": *insipiencia jumentorum stupenda bestialitate transcendens* . . .

In the religious guise of the Crusades, bloodied, gorged with plunder—under the banner of the Cross, the elite of Europe's nobility launched itself eight times against Palestine "to liberate the Holy Sepulchre." In the wake of their armies, whole towns turned out on foot, peregrinating across the Mediterranean to renew their baptism in the waters of the Jordan: an arduous odyssey from West to East.

1118

The first Crusade already dated a century when Hugues de Payns and eight other French noblemen who had journeyed to the Holy Land presented themselves to the Patriarch of Jerusalem before whom they pledged their lives to police the roads leading into Palestine for the protection of defence of the pilgrims from the Saracens, to guard the desert wells and serve the King's knighthood. For this modest mission, they vowed themselves to combat the enemies of God "in obedience, chastity and poverty."

Nine at the beginning, they served for nine years without subjecting themselves to any regulations and without assuming religious habit, living from alms and preceding the pilgrims whenever they were needed, curious adjunct to the Christian armies in the Orient.

"A new knighthood has appeared in the Land of the Incarnation. It is new, I say, and not yet proved in the world where it leads a double combat, sometimes against adversaries of flesh and blood, sometimes against the spirit of evil in the heavens. And that these knights resist their bodily enemies by the force of their bodies I do not consider to be marvellous because I do not consider it rare, but that they wage war by the force of the spirit against vices and demons, I would call that not only marvellous, but worthy of all praise accorded to monks," wrote Saint Bernard of Clairvaux on behalf of Hugues de Payns, first Master of the eight.

Beaudouin II and the Patriarch viewed the establishment of the Order with pleasure and were sympathetic to these noblemen who had abandoned everything for

The temple *(ph. Bulloz)*.

Christ, and drawing great benefit from the knights in their expeditions, they protected the Order and gave it certain properties to provide for its needs. And because they had no church or dwelling of their own, the knights were lodged in the King's palace, next to the ancient site of the Temple of Solomon—razed by Nebuchadnezzar—from whence they took their name of Templars.

1128

The knights were officially established as a military and religious Order at the Council of Troyes, which fixed their Statute and accorded them the right to wear white robes. The rules prohibited immoderate abstinences, encouraging the knightage to keep rigorously fit, and privileged them to possess and manage property in spite of their vows of poverty. Their number increased so rapidly that there were soon more than three hundred white-robed knights in their assemblies.

As recompense for their services throughout the Crusades, they eventually acquired immense properties on both sides of the sea, possessing whole cities and palaces, enriching themselves still further by the revenue thereof, and by the commerce of money. With the soaring growth of the Order as an independent power, it owned, at the beginning of the XIVth century, nine thousand fortified castles and property in every capital of Christendom. Besides accumulating all kinds of immunities from the Church, a succession of sovereigns had added an exceptional liberty to their wealth, slowly exciting an envy across two centuries which finally came to provoke the greed of Philip IV the Fair, feudal king of France, and led him to unite with a Pope to destroy the Order.

In lauding the Templars for their self-abnegation, Saint Bernard had made their fortune, and through a traffic in these riches, the Order of the Temple became a kind of international bank, opening accounts, lending indiscriminately to sovereigns and consequently active in diplomacy. It also served as a changing house for those pilgrims departing for the Holy Land who, instead of risking the dangers of transporting money, made deposits with the Templars in Europe and received the equivalent sum upon presenting a receipt in Palestine.

With the final loss of Jerusalem, the Crusades came to an inglorious end and the Order emigrated to Europe, establishing the French Temple, in Paris, where it occupied an entire district with the old

Temple enclosed within walls. The new Temple stood on the outside with its tower housing that part of the royal treasure which the Templars kept for Philip IV, while they themselves remained vowed to poverty, for any money found in the effects of a deceased knight caused him to be denied burial service and to be interred in common ground.

1306

The sumptuous Paris headquarters was often used to lodge important guests of France, and the King himself sought refuge in its tower when menaced by a population outraged by his last devaluation.

More than once had Philip the Fair resorted to iniquitous means to procure money for his increasingly energetic government, to wage war on the English and crush the Flemish revolt. He levied wholesale taxes and, arbitrarily modifying the value of his coins, falsified the exchange. His sojourn in the Temple enlightened him not only on the riches of the Order, but upon its own incredible unpopularity, for the people detested the Templars because of their prosperity, and the secrecy with which they surrounded their activities had for long provoked the most hostile rumours.

And the King did not remain indifferent to the treasures which the knights had amassed by that time, and after having plundered the Lombards and persecuted the Jews of the kingdom "to the limit of what the traffic would bear," it occurred to him that in addition to being bankers, the Order held immense landed estates which, with the Pope's assistance, he might acquire. Always sensitized to insinuations of avarice, Philip even took the trouble of absolving himself of cupidity when later confiscating the Templar's funds and liberating himself of his huge debts to their House.

But most particularly did the Order's independence interfere with his plans for state control, and it seemed a propitious time for the Church to discover that the knights had fallen into heresy.

With the aid of his lieutenant, Guillaume de Nogaret, Philip had already led a campaign of defamation against Pope Boniface VIII, who had been imprudent enough to enter into conflict with the King of France. The combination served both to destroy the Pontiff and generally intimidate his successor, Clement V.

Excluded from Rome, Clement received his tiara in France, upon which ceremony a wall supporting numerous spectators collapsed, killing several citizens and knocking the new Pope from his horse. Having dropped his crown in the fall and losing one of its precious stones, the people augured ill for his reign, and it was a demoralized Pontiff who took up residence in Avignon. During the trial of the Templars, he lived at Poitiers as a guest of the King, who opposed the spiritual authority with discretion and even presented himself as a defender of the exiled Bishop of Rome—an addict of nepotism and simony.

Although Philip the Fair viewed the Templars as a corporation simultaneously ecclesiastic, financial and military, forming an enclave in the state which he wished to unite, the Order presented no political threat, for it numbered no more than 15,000 knights or sergeants; nor was it a religious danger, for the so-called confessions of heresy, extracted under torture, are contradictory. The dossier compiled by the legalists is now proved to have had no probative value, revealing that the affair was wholly corrupt from its start.

But the prestige of the Order had suffered, as did other military Orders, from the disasters of the Christians in the Orient: even the monk-soldiers were accused of having sold the Holy Land to the Saracens and legends had formed concerning their avidity and the strange activities behind the Temple walls.

There had been other sovereigns presented with the first rumours regarding the Order but they had either refused to listen, or else demanded immediate proof. When Philip IV was approached, he quickly converted the gossip into first accusations, bravely affirming that all the charges were proved, for he had only to believe in the excesses of the Templars in order to feel "obliged" to end their shameful practices.

Thus, motivated by a financial crisis and reaction to a power which challenged royal power itself, the extermination of the Order was conceived.

In attacking the Templars, Philip and his lieutenants undertook a hazardous operation, perpetrating their act under the cloak of a juridical instrument. The idea of suppressing the least religious community was difficult in the spirit of the times, for the change might bring about reform, rather than elimination. To justify the destruction of the Order, it was necessary to prove it to be horribly perverted in essence and to have been so for some time. The martyrdom of Saint Joan was similarly "justi-

Seals of the Templars *(ph. E. Janet Le Caisne)*.

fied," and the measures taken to attach inflammable material to her body were not designed to intensify her agony, but better to assure a total destruction by fire, preventing the people from making relics of her bones. In Victorian raiment, the same infected logic served Sir Roger Casement's enemies, and the enemies of the Irish cause, for whom it was not only necessary that Casement die, but that he die a dishonoured man. The Black Diaries were introduced after the benighted rebel had been sentenced to hang for high treason and were used in such a manner as to alienate sympathy, and make a reprieve impossible.

Since the basis of the Order of the Templars was initiatory and not religious, its double face permitted those who judged it to cheat,

and still permits historians to monger in the scandal that phoenixed from its autos-da-fé.

When Philip the Fair decided to brave the powerful papacy and win over the new Pope, who found the accusations "improbable and incredible," he decided to place the affair of the Templars in the hands of de Nogaret, who had so well succeeded in slandering Pope Boniface, even after that unfortunate Pontiff had actually excommunicated the King.

It was merely a matter of locating renegade or expulsed knights who had "lost the House" by their misconduct and wished to avenge themselves, for in addition to the services of the wheel, the whip, rack and pillory, Philip wielded the most potent instrument of authority commanded by sovereigns in the Middle

35

Ages—the *placita legalia,* a private inquisition whereby subjects were forced to describe, singly and in secret, the details of all crimes and offences within their knowledge.

1307

In August, a winnowing of possible informers finally produced a knight who accused the Order with the capital crime of apostasy.

The Templars must have sensed the mounting storm, for they took at least one decision, and in August of 1307, the Pope announced to the King that at the request of Jacques de Molay, Grand Master of the Order, he was opening an inquiry on the subject of the Temple.

On September 23, at Maubuisson, de Nogaret received the keeping of the Great Seal of France, becoming the prime instrument of Philip in his war upon the Order, and the mandate of the knights' arrest is dated the 14th of September, Maubuisson.

At a given hour on October 13, it was executed, and all the Templars of France were simultaneously arrested—with the sanction of the Pope, now diplomatically allied with Philip, signalling the beginning of the trial which ended in March, 1314, with the ordeal of Jacques de Molay, burned alive, Place Dauphine, after fifty-four other Templars had already perished at the stake for having retracted their confessions.

The king's men who performed the arrests were ordered to present themselves with a force sufficient enough to deter resistance, and certain dignitaries of the Temple were located and seized in the King's very presence—indeed, de Molay had attended a funeral the day before, standing at the side of his sovereign.

The requisition prepared for the occasion already contained all of the eighty-seven accusations brought against the Order, phrased in their most exaggerated form, chiefly charging: clandestine and nocturnal ceremonies of admission with a ritual consisting of *baisers obscènes,* renunciation of Christ with blasphemous outrage of the crucifix and solemn oath by the Holy Sacrament never to divulge the Order's secrets. More specifically, it was charged that the knights had become Mohammedans in secret and that the elders worshipped an idol in provincial chapters, while at the ceremony of reception, initiate was ordered to kiss initiator on the spine, the navel and the mouth, and to practice homosexuality, which accounts for the accusation not merely of sodomy, but of *obligatory* sodomy.

The new knight was then to don a small cord, first placed about the idol, which would have symbolized inversion. But these famous "cordelettes" were, *in fine,* chastity belts, emblematic of their vows of abstention, and highly commended by Saint Bernard, who expounded on the "dung-heap of the flesh."

A preliminary inquest was made by the Inquisitioner of France before the King ordered the seizure of the Templars and their property. The King's agents immediately proceeded to examine the prisoners, after which they placed them under guard, and only then did they summon the Commissary of the Holy Office, who instructed his investigators to interrogate them diligently "for the truth, by torture, if necessary." It was recommended that the procedure be halted at the stage of *territio,* or questioning under *threat* of torture. In such cases, the prisoners were brought to the torture chamber and confronted with the executioner, who showed them the instruments whose action on the body was described in great detail. At this point, a final chance to confess was offered and if the "truth" was then disclosed (that is, if confession tallied with accusation) their depositions would be recorded and notarized. Copies of these confessions would be imme-diately sent to the King, which is to say that protestations of innocence would be suppressed.

The accused were then exhorted on the articles of faith and told that both Pope and King were reliably informed of the error and sodomy they had committed, particularly upon initiation, and pardon was promised if they confessed. Those who were seduced by this offer and lacked the courage to retract their statements later reappeared as eyewitness-denunciators against their co-accused. Normally, the Templars were only permitted to "confess" to chaplains of the Order, and dared not discuss the admission rites even among themselves. The threat of death as relapsed heretics awaited those who confessed and later recanted, and it was upon this simple formula, perfected in the Middle Ages, that Joan of Arc was burned and Galileo silenced.

The sight of the torture chamber was such that a great many knights broke down at the stage of *territio,* and speedily confessed all or in part to the compromising practices considered either sacrilegious or merely "dangerous to the public order." The precision and crudity of the terms employed to characterize the Templars' morals were likewise such that the enormity of the accusations would seem to guarantee perfect concordance. But in spite of the irregularities of procedure, there were retractions and discrepancies of testimony, each disclosure in itself being of horrifying precision. The racks of the Inquisition strained with Templars.

The articles of error thus extracted from several knights avowed that, upon initiation, the Master led them behind the sacristy and, showing them a crucifix, made them repudiate Christ and spit thrice upon the Cross. After ordering the initiate to cast off his robe, his receiver then placed a kiss at the base of the spine, below the belt and upon the mouth, and declared that if any brother of the Order wished to lie with him carnally, he must suffer it according to the Statute of the Order. Further they confessed that several among them had lain with one another carnally, for they claimed they had been encouraged to take the pleasures of warriors.

And they confessed that each one was belted with a small cord which the brothers "must wear as long as they lived," and it was understood that these cords had been placed about an idol in the form of a man's head, but that this was not known to all the brothers.

In the three extant copies of the

Engraved motif appearing on a Moslem box found in Essarois, France, with alleged representation of Baphomet (*Bibliothèque Nationale, Paris*).

Order's strict Rules, sodomy is indicated as a capital misdeed to be severely punished. The accusation went so far as to claim that they sometimes nourished themselves on children. The majority of the charges collapsed before the responses of the accused.

Different versions were extracted from the prisoners but the principle remains the same: sodomy was "imposed," by whom, no one knew, and it was "obligatory," a word familiar to the tools of the Holy Office.

The Inquisitors themselves must have found the third accusation too ridiculous in its original form, because the knights were accused of giving, not of receiving, kisses. There was but one, in fact, at the time of initiation, and it was more of what would now be considered an accolade; yet, on the basis of such a charge, the Order was finally judged and condemned.

1307

Taken off guard before the enormity and unlikelihood of the accusations, tormented and baited, the Templars staggered. They had been shown an alleged confession of apostasy by the Grand Master, and even letters in which he recommended that they also confess. Most of the French Templars were only brother-sergeants, simple and un-lettered men, but the knights themselves made no good showing. Out of forty-nine Templars interrogated in Paris (in the lower room of their own House) during that October and November, there were only three who confessed to nothing. The confessions of the Master and the leading dignitaries caused a scandal and threw almost ineffaceable suspicions on the Temple. From then on, the defence of the Order was difficult, its farflung champions panicked and no longer dared to testify in favour of the knights.

The form of the confessions having been established in advance, it is not surprising that the testimony generally agreed, but the descriptions of the idol reputedly worshipped by the elders varied with each admission, while still sufficiently complementing in the charges of idolatry, demonology and sorcery, and unorthodox enough to have contributed to the ruin of the Templars on those grounds. "Treated" by the Inquisition, all magic became heresy; the persecution led by the Church against sorcery anticipated its battle against Science, and the Church has not yet reputiated its mediæval doctrines on the subject.

As soon as the Templars were simultaneously arrested, the Chief Inquisitioner of Paris instructed his agents to interrogate the prisoners about an idol of a bearded human head which during the trial was refered to as 'Baphomet".

For some of the accused it was a wooden figure, for others, of silver or copper—or stone; some saw it as a female, others, male—bald or hirsute, double-headed. For some it had the aspect of a cat with one face, two, or three. Those who spoke agreed only that the head was terrifying and Inquisitors and

Saladin, Sultan of Egypt *(ph. Giraudon)*.

Portrait of Jacques de Molay *(ph. Giraudon)*.

prisoners equally lost footing, for obviously no one quite understood what it pertained to, since the descriptions were drawn from confessions, taking on increasingly fantastic forms until the object of their cult presented itself as the dismaying shape of Satan himself.

The Order's figure, however, never was an idol but a synthetic image, a hieroglyph, in which the Templars grouped the elements of their tradition, and as emblem of that tradition, was particularly employed outside of the Temple as an esoteric paradigm, seal of chivalry and sign of recognition. Such baphometic images have survived.

The "idol" thus presenting such a grossly animal form, doubtless explains the diversity of its descriptions and it is therefore astonishing that although the Templars were arrested at the same hour, there was no seizure of a single image corresponding to the accusation and the confessions. One figure was produced before the Holy Office—a very large and beautiful head having "the contours of a woman," and containing two small bones which some claimed to belong to one of the Eleven Thousand Virgins. Clearly, under torture, several knights were driven to speak of relics as diabolical idols, giving rise to so many extravagant interpretations of what, at the beginning, was only a declaration of compliance, devoid of basis, fixing a religious or metaphysical liaison between the Moslems and the Templars, for the very name "Baphomet" stems from the confession of a Templar-sergeant from Languedoc in whose peculiar tongue the word "Mohammed" could very well sound.

Some theories regarding the name would have it a cabal in itself, a phonetic device employed throughout the Middle Ages by philosophers and diplomats. Knights, trouvères, troubadours and minstrels comprised the "chevalerie," or "cabalerie", . . . mediæval argot, mediæval "art gothique".

There were XIXth-century scholars who declared that the Templars' image was hermaphroditic, as it appeared on certain chests which had just been discovered, coffers containing Arab medicines. An androgynous divinity being nothing else than an archaic formula expressing both male-female, positive-negative principles by bi-sexuality, such hermetic androgynes are an extremely common phenomenon in cults of the sacred.

The French historian Ollivier, would have the name stemming from Bapho, a port of Cyprus where the Templars had long sojourned and where, in antiquity, there had been a temple dedicated to Astarte—or Ishtar, simultaneously Venus, the Moon, Virgin and mother, adored under the form of a black stone, accompanied by infant sacrifice, as with the rites to Baal. It is certain that the Templars' Baphomet was not literally of stone, for there were specific interdictions on the part of mediæval kings and clergy concerning the cult of stones, and, above all, against seminal emission in front of stones.

To the Templars, the "ma-donna" represented the liaison between earth and heaven, allying fecundity and purity, and the cult which they dedicated to "Notre Dame Sainte Marie" was not a "sublimation of courtly love," but an exaltation of that more carnal love of the troubadour for his Lady. Indeed the errant knights returning from the East exerted a great moral influence on Europe in instilling the idea of chivalry by the idealized influence of the mediæval woman. One of the most memorable results of the Crusades was this importation of the idea of romantic love which, preached by the Virgin-worshipping troubadours, transformed a loutish nobility into a polished society of courtly lords and ladies, and gave rise to what were called the Courts of Love.

With the mediæval lord more often away at war than at home in his chateau, the chatelaines of Languedoc and Provence, in order to stave off boredom, invented those tribunals composed of women, illustrious by birth or learning, whose jurisdiction extended over all questions and responses concerning gallantry, courtesy and love. Knights, poets and troubadours were in attendance, and the Courts of Love in gothic France yielded the decrees based on the code of a certain André, court chaplain of the XIIth century, entitled: *De arte amatoria et reprobatione amoris.*

It was also through the Crusades that the cult of the Virgin was brought to "merry" England— through Compostella, by poor pilgrims bearing palm-branches, with copies of the apocryphal Gospels in their wallets and Aphrodite's scallop shell stitched to their hats.

The Templars were always suspected of having derived some of their "secret rites and vices" from religious and political sects in Syria and Egypt with whom they were, in fact, in constant contact. Among these sects in particular was the formidable brotherhood of the Ismaelians, or "assassins" whose sect sprung up in the mountains of XIth century Persia and was ruled by an old man, or lord of the mountain.

The direct contact between Templars and Ismaelians is well established, and we know this contact alternated between "implacable duel and a rather suspect fraternization," for when the Crusades invaded the Holy Land, built castles and settled down, they found, living there under Moslem protection, a number of heretical Christian sects who soon seduced them from orthodoxy. And in confronting the Saracens, who held themselves to spread the Mohammedan faith throughout the world, the Templars met a complementary brotherhood and addressed their enthusiasm to Arab science, then at its pinnacle, and it was through the Crusade of the XIIth century that the majority of ancient Oriental knowledge was brought into Europe. Through the intermediary of the Templars, the Arab conquest had a considerable civilizing role for the West which later determined in Christianity an irresistible élan towards Islam and its mysterious promisers. In its spirit, practices, intentions, and even in its complex substance, the popular Christianity of the West is but a syncretic paganism in Oriental trappings.

The residence of the Grand

Master of the Temple was in Jerusalem until its seizure by the Saladins, which is to say time enough to ripen suspicions of affiliation, including the imputation of *catharsis* with which the Templars were also charged, and which had already caused a scandal with the Albigenses, who had embraced Aristotle's idea of purging the soul of sordid ideas and desires. The Cathars admitted two equal principles, God and Satan, the first being the creator of the invisible, spiritual and eternal world, while the second created and governed the material, temporal world. For them, Christ was not a man but a pure figure. The Cathars of Albi rejected the sacraments, the sacrifice of the mass, intercession of the Virgin and the saints, the relics and indulgences and in general all of the Catholic practices, engaging in the most severe asceticism. Their religious extremes proved to lend themselves to charges of heresy and it was thus not only in the Holy Land that the Church had to combat the *infidèles,* but in France, where *catharsis* had taken such root as to be embraced by both the nobles and the people.

Themselves great builders of kraks, or fortified chateaux, and as builders of Temples, the knights entertained cordial relations of "initiates to initiates" with the builders of those French cathedrals whose transparent Persian carpets and wheeling roses sign the liaison between the Templars and Islam, and also between the Order and those craftsmen known as Free Masons. The Crusades to the Holy Land were replaced with Crusades of cathedral building, and special dispensations were made to those who built them, a new guise for pilgrimage.

After the catastrophic trial and execution of the Templars, the Grand Master of Auvergne fled with several knights. Disguising themselves as stone masons to avoid recognition, they took refuge on a Scottish island, whence the geographical source of the Scottish rites, and, as the "hereditary masons of the Templars," pursued the tradition of the Order and undertook the "vengeance of de Molay."

Jacques de Molay was arrested with the other Templars and his first confessions are elusive and reticent. The judges awaited a complete submission with unrestricted confessions, and the Grand Master rescinded his statements several times. The most troubling element at this point stemmed from his attitude, and that of the Grand Bailiff of the Order; both baited by the Inquisitioner for testimony fatal to the

Temple. Torture was not applied. but de Molay's last retraction indicates the employment of *territio,* for he accused himself of having lied out of fear of the torments, and not because of them, demanding, even, to be tortured so that his brothers would not believe he had destroyed the Order voluntarily. He was told that there were public witnesses against him, eliminating the need of torture, and it appears indeed that he weakened at the sight of the instruments.

Under oath, he declared that when he had been received into the Order forty-two years earlier, he had made several promises relative to the observances and statutes of the knights. A bronze Cross had been brought into his presence, bearing the image of Christ, and when told to deny Christ as the true prophet, he did so in spite of himself, and when asked to spit upon the Cross, he spit on the ground. Confessing to the same accusation, Geoffroy de Gonneville, preceptor of Aquitania and a Templar for twenty-eight years, said that the practice of spitting on the Cross was introduced by a promise made during the Crusades in the Holy Land. A Master of the Order had been a prisoner of the Sultan, who promised him liberation after he swore to impose the act upon the Templars. But if such a ritual existed, it was certainly more ancient than the Order, and it is probable that it had another meaning entirely. In terms of initiation, the spitting on the Crucifix would have been as much a test as the very trial itself was to the Order.

Interrogated on the point of whether or not, when he took his vows of chastity, he was encouraged to unite carnally with his brothers, de Molay replied under oath that he was not, and yet, twenty hours after the first interrogation, he renounced pleading the cause of his Order and asked to be brought before the Pope.

The confessions made three days earlier by Geoffroy de Charnay, Preceptor of Normandy, were much more compromising, and have the air of deriving from torture. When interrogated about the kisses, he stated under oath that he had kissed the Master who received him into the Order, and that he had heard the Preceptor of Auvergne tell the brothers of that chapter to unite with each other, rather than debauch themselves with women, but that he himself had never done so, and it was not required.

Most lamentable of all were the confessions of Hugues de Pairaud, who admitted to spitting on the Cross, to the *baisers obscènes,* acknowledging himself to be guilty of having received several brothers with a shameful ceremony and even to have counselled morals against Nature. He reappeared after a suspension of the session—indicating further application of torture in order to aggravate his confessions, for he went on to recognize the adoration of the human-headed idol and, most disconcerting of all, he confessed to apostasy.

When the Holy Office later relinquished the idea of attributing a positive heretic doctrine to the Templars, their apostasy became a gratuitous act, absurd, with no *raison d'être,* and without consequence. From one end of the interrogation to the other, each Templar protested that he had denied God in space, from the mouth and not from the heart, and that he did not spit "weepingly upon a Cross proffered by a groaning Commander," but that he had spit upon the ground.

Each knight protested that he was a good Christian and believed in his companions' reverence, and none admitted to having received esoteric instruction, the very concept of which must have been alien to them, for they lived at a time when the lack of books demanded the oral transmission of *any* knowledge. By the XIVth century, furthermore,

the prestige, obedience and the social mission of the Order found itself implicated by the procession of events. The Latin territory became more and more a base of international commerce and lost its sacred character, and the Order's transplantation from Jerusalem to France cut off its spiritual lifeline with the atmosphere of Islam.

At the end, those who mounted the pyre died in proclaiming their innocence. It was not the confession of guilt that led to their destruction, but the very protestation of innocence—not for crimes committed, but for retracted testimony.

On the 25th of October, before an assembly which included the Templars, Jacques de Molay made a public confession to the effect he had not wished to confess his crimes for fear of temporal punishments— and not because of them, and for fear the Order would be destroyed and the knights deprived of the honours of this world, "but he who made light, from whom nothing is hidden," had brought them into the open through the intermediary of King Philip. This declaration can only be explained as the hope of de Molay and his lieutenants to extricate themselves from the affair and to save the lives of the Templars by abject submission from which, with the Pope's assistance, they expected to eventually recover.

Clement V vacillated. By the Bulle Pastoralis, he had sanctioned the arrest of the Templars in all countries, and the papal orders were carried out by the Princes of England, Spain and Germany, although only in France was the stake dressed for the knights.

Towards the end of 1307, the Pope requested that Philip place the French Templars in the hands of two Cardinals who were subsequently sent to the Castle of Chinon, where the accused were under guard. Their presence so encouraged de Molay and Pairaud that they revoked their confessions and even managed to send wax tablets to the other detained knights, with warnings to follow their example.

When Clement finally decided to break the power of the Inquisitors and place the matter before the Curia, the King's resentment made itself felt through the thoroughfares of his dungeons and again, soon afterwards, the knights returned to their first confessions, admitting to all of the charges and demanding absolution—which the Cardinals accorded them and petitioned Philip for the Templars' pardon.

But even if the Pope believed the Order innocent, he could not guarantee the purity of its members, and since those knights who had experienced the King's procedures had admitted at least once to being heretics, the Church would seriously compromise itself by undertaking their defence.

Troubled by certain testimonies, either forced or fabricated, the papal pendulum swung back to diplomatic reconciliation with the King, the Order's greatest adversary.

With Clement no longer wishing to aid them, and despite their ramifications in other countries, the Templars of France found themselves isolated and without means. In abandoning hope, they could only recognize what was mercilessly demanded of them, and accept life imprisonment if they wished to live.

1312–1314

In March, 1312, at the Council of Troyes, the Pope pronounced the suppression and extinction of the Order of the Templars, daring to declare that any member of the Council who raised his voice without permission would be excommunicated. The knights found guilty received individual sentences, while the judgment of the Master and the leading dignitaries of the Order was to drag out for another two years before they were led, emaciated and ravaged, onto the parvis of Notre-Dame to hear the sentence passed upon them by the apostolic delegates. The Order of the Temple had existed for two centuries, its trial for seven years, and it had been four years since Jacques de Molay had been seen in public. The sentence of life imprisonment was read aloud before the Parisians who had amassed in silence, but the reading was hardly over when de Molay and Charnay turned towards the people, crying out that the confessions, the crimes and heresies imputed to the Order were false, that the Temple was "sainte, juste et Catholique" and that they had confessed to save their lives. According to the Florentine chronicler, a sergeant of the King put his hand over the Master's mouth to check this outcry, and the crowd showed itself disturbed by these unexpected declarations. The Cardinals then placed the two relapsed heretics in the hands of the Provost of Paris, in order to discharge the measures to be taken, for the Church never inflicted the death penalty: the Inquisition handed its condemned over to the secular authorities, with a recommendation of mercy.

As soon as he was informed of what had happened, Philip gave the order to immediately burn alive, at slow fire, the two Templars who had refused to compromise, and to profit of the flames by including thirty-seven other knights equally too resistant. The Templars' last request was that they might die with their faces turned towards Notre-Dame, and in the spring twilight, to the creeping anguish of the stake, the last convulsive efforts of Jacques de Molay went to summon both the Pope and the King to appear before the divine tribunal before the year was out.

Clement V died the next month and when Philip the Fair followed him in November, a chronicle reports that, at autopsy, the King's heart proved to be so small that it could have been that of a newborn child, or of a bird.

BIBLIOGRAPHY

Albert OLLIVIER: *Les Templiers* (Paris, 1958).

Marion MELVILLE: *La Vie des Templiers* (Paris, 1951).

Jean GIMPEL: *Les Bâtisseurs de Cathédrales* (Paris, 1958).

Joseph CALMETTE: *Le Moyen Age* (Paris, 1948).

Robert GRAVES: *The White Goddess* (London, 1948).

Matila C. GHYKA: *Le Nombre d' Or* (Paris, 1931).

THE EAGLE AS A LOVER
Some further conquests of
Napoleon Bonaparte
by ERIC KAHANE

"I awake full of you. Your portrait and the memory of yesterday's intoxicating evening have given my senses no pause. Sweet and incomparable Josephine, what a strange effect you have upon my heart! Are you angry? Do I see you sad? Are you worried? Then my soul is shattered with pain and there is no rest for your friend . . . But can there be any rest for me when, as we surrender ourselves to the deep feeling which o'erpowers me, I draw from your lips, from your heart, a flame which burns me. Ah! How well did I see last night that your portrait is not you and . . . You are leaving at noon. I shall see you within three hours. In the meantime, *mio dolce amor,* receive a million kisses, but give me none lest it set fire to my blood.

B."

This was Napoleon's first letter to Josephine, sent from Paris, at "7 o'clock in the morning," and hastily scrawled after their first night of love, sometime in October or November 1795. He was then twenty-six years of age, she was thirty-two. He saw in her the highest archetype of Woman while she thought of him as only a temporary lover among many others. He was an ignorant and blundering Daphnis, and she was far too worldly wise and far too calculating to play at Chloe. He was a virgin in spirit and hardly less so in body, and she was the half-naked queen of the Directoire—that decaying society where everything, conscience and flesh alike, was up for auction, where upstarts, Incroyables and Merveilleuses had no other *raisons d'être* but stockjobbery, speculation, blackmail and debauchery. Napoleon's only ambition was to marry Josephine and lead with her "the life of a decent middle-class couple," while *her* ambition was to get whatever profit she could from the sudden rise to power of the young and candid general.

For Napolione Buonaparte—he had not yet Frenchified his Italian name—was already on the threshold of his career. He was born in Corsica on the 15th of August, 1769 (exactly one year before the island became French), the son of a country squire and of an austere, superstitious and half-illiterate matron; he spent his childhood years in the military academies of the kingdom, alone with his books, scorned by his classmates who poked fun at his harsh Mediterranean accent and his impossible name. At sixteen, donning the uniform of an artillery lieutenant, he wandered from garrison town to garrison town—dreaming of heroic deeds and fantastic battles but accomplishing nothing. For eight long years, while monarchy was foundering on the gallows, while the newly born Republic was at war with nearly all the European powers—giving out generals' stars to junior officers like himself—Bonaparte was almost exclusively engaged in mere police tasks against rioters armed with cudgels and pitchforks.

Then, losing faith in his future, he decided to resign his commission—and suddenly, a few hours before leaving the country to become an instructor in the Turkish army, he was ordered to subdue a royalist-inspired riot in Paris. He opened fire on the mob with such cold-blooded precision that he was promoted overnight to military governor of the capital.

It was at this time, in the fall of 1795, that he met Josephine and fell hopelessly in love for the first time in his life. Before her, there had been only a few affairs, either platonic or sordid. As a young second lieutenant, he had had an idyll with the daughter of a provincial noblewoman, Caroline du Colombier: "Nothing could have been more innocent," he told his biographer Las Cases some thirty years later. "I still remember a tryst . . . All our pleasure boiled down to eating cherries together."

He was eighteen when he sowed his wild oats; it happened on the 22nd of November, 1787, and he immediately wrote a lengthy account of it, at once complacent and oddly prudish—for his initiator was one of the innumerable prostitutes keeping open shop at the Palais-Royal:

". . . I was on the threshold of one of these iron gates when my gaze fell upon a person of the fair sex. The time, her demeanour, her great youth did not allow me to doubt that she was a woman of pleasure . . . But her pale cast, the frailty of her figure and her soft voice did not leave me a moment's peace. Here, I told myself, is some-

Letter of credit for 25 kisses.

one who can be useful to me in the experiment that I wish to make— or she is but a clod-hopper . . ." She told him she was named Madeleine and hailed from Nantes, in Brittany. " 'I know that place,' he said. 'Mad, you must do me the pleasure of telling me how you lost your cherry.' 'It was an officer took it,' was the girl's classic reply, and she added: 'Let's go to your place.' 'What shall we do there?' 'Come, we'll get warm by the fire and you will satisfy your need.' I was far from becoming scrupulous. I had teased her so that I knew she would not run off when she would be pressed by the argument that I was preparing—with a sincerity which she would soon discover I did not have . . ."

Here the story ended abruptly. This relation bore already the stamp of the future Emperor: a man wavering between lyricism and scur- rility, naïveté and intolerance, misogyny and sexual greed. After this first and apparently unhappy experience, several years elapsed before Bonaparte admitted to a new affair—this time with the wife of a Deputy, a Félicité Turreau who, as he recalled later, "had fair hair, spirit, patriotism and philosophy." Félicité was accompanying her husband on an inspection tour on the Italian border. To bedazzle her, Bonaparte—who had recently been promoted to brigadier —decided to "treat her to the spectacle of war," and he gave orders to attack the Italian outposts. "This skirmish was pure fantasy," he said later to Las Cases, "and yet a few men were killed . . . Every time I remember this day, I feel deeply ashamed." Be it as it may, this exhibition impressed Madame Turreau and the young General was generously rewarded, although this new experience did not give him what he later called "the revelation of love."

At twenty-five, his views on women still showed a strangely childish harshness, ill-acquired through the theories of Jean-Jacques Rousseau. His was the philosophy of a narrow-minded bourgeois moralist: man should get married to have children as well as to quench a purely sensual urge; woman's only function is to keep house, submit to her husband and bring up his children. As for love, it is but a dangerous chimera: "I believe love is harmful to mankind," he wrote when he was twenty; "it does far more evil than good, and some benevolent deity should rid us of it and thus deliver the world."

Elsewhere, he denounced "the illusory pleasures of the senses: firstly, they put man's machinery out of order; but above all, they deprive him of the purity, the moral sensibility and the scrupulousness of a good conscience." Thus, to young Bonaparte, there could be no true love, even in wedlock, and no concession should ever be made to the chosen bedmate. On this second point at least, his opinion remained the same throughout his life, and in Saint Helena he told Las Cases: "Woman belongs to us as the fruit-tree belongs to the gardener . . . Nature has made women our slaves; it is only through a whim of ours that they are allowed to rule over us."

In 1794, while purporting these rigidly austere theories, more befitting a mediæval hermit than a young artillery officer, Bonaparte became suddenly infatuated with the daughter of a wealthy merchant from Marseilles, Désirée Clary. She was a rather plain-looking girl, but she was pure, submissive and quiet, and had all the makings of a good housewife. Under the delusion that he had found the ideal bride, Bonaparte soon proposed to her— which did not stop him from raping her—and they were officially engaged when he was recalled to Paris. And there, in a matter of days, he forgot Désirée and fell head over heels in love with the most dangerous incarnation of the Femme Fatale: Rose-Josephine Tascher de la Pagerie, Viscountess de Beauharnais.

She was a Creole woman from Martinique, married at the age of fifteen, divorced at twenty, mother of two grown-up children and the semi-official mistress of the most powerful man in France, the Director Paul Barras. She had a pretty face and full rounded lips hiding yellowish and poorly-kept teeth; her body was slim and soft, admirably broken in to the most skilful refinements of bedplay; her mind was at once indolent and covetous, and perfectly cynical. She had an irrepressible taste for finery and luxury, and she periodically accumulated a fortune in debts. She was a businesswoman as well as a woman of pleasure, ready to love whoever was in love with her—and could keep her well. She was living on borrowed money, bribes, and underhanded deals, and it was only the influence or the complicity of her lovers that kept her out of bankruptcy and prison.

Bonaparte knew all this and he did not care, stunned as he was by the discovery of a sexual thrill which he had never experienced before, or even imagined possible; it was no longer a brutal and quickspent urge but a deep, constantly renewed ecstasy. Overwhelmed by a blind and somewhat masochistic passion, he forgave her misbehaviour, her past and even her countless lovers: "If you had been younger and less naïve, I should have loved you less," he wrote her during the spring of 1796, and in another letter he said: "I loved everything about you, even the memory of your short-comings." Yet he attempted in a rather strange way to "purify" her by christening her anew; he made her relinquish her first name—which so many lovers, known and un-known, had used—and thus Rose became Josephine.

As deeply in love as he was, Bonaparte was still quite aware that his own career would benefit greatly from his affair with Josephine. In these times of political instability, when the whole country was wavering between the Revolution and the Empire, Josephine was on a good footing with both the old and the new regime. She was of noble birth and had made her debuts in the pre-revolutionary society of Versailles—and now she was equally at ease as the Viscountess de Beauharnais as a Citizeness sharing the couch of Republican Sans - Culottes. With shameless realism, Bonaparte used Josephine's high position to raise himself up, knowing full well that marrying her would step up his own future. Barras, as a matter of fact, had grown tired of his mistress and was only too happy to hand her over to his protégé Bonaparte—to whom he promised as well, as a token of gratitude, the high command of the French army in Italy.

In the meantime—perhaps to make Josephine jealous and thus bind her more securely to himself—Bonaparte was openly having an affair with a Mrs. Permon, the over-ripe widow of an army contractor. Under the guise of "checking up on Parisian opinion," he was taking her to the theatre practically every night, and there he courted the good lady with soldierly rashness. The widow's daughter, who was to become the Duchess of Abrantès, wrote later in her *Memoirs* that "those who had sworn to Bonaparte's faithfulness [to Josephine] had not seen him blush, pale, tremble, even shed tears. There used to be a box at the old Théâtre Feydeau, at the first railing, much wiser on this subject . . ."

At long last, Josephine gave in—and on the dawn of the 11th of March, 1796, two days after his wedding, Bonaparte left Paris for Nice, whence he was to lead an army of tatterdemalions to the conquest of Italy. During the next few weeks, he gave battle almost every day, winning dazzling victories, bending generals and rulers to his will. And at night, every night, he sent Josephine endless and pathetic letters:

"Every second takes me farther away from you," he wrote on the day of his departure, "and every second I find less courage to be away from you . . ." "Adieu, adieu, I go to bed without you, I shall sleep without you. I beg of you, let me sleep. For the past several nights, I felt you in my arms, happy dream, but—but you were not there . . ." "Do you remember that dream in which I took off your shoes, your frills, and I made you enter inside my heart . . .?" Thus he rambled on every day, alternatively sentimental and crude: "Good God! How happy I would be if I could be there while you are dressing—a little shoulder, a small breast, white, firm, elastic, and above, your little face with a kerchief à la Creole, good enough to eat. You know I have not forgotten the little visits—you know, the little black woods! I give it a thousand kisses and await with impatience the moment I shall be within . . . To live in a Josephine is to live in Paradise. A kiss on your mouth, a kiss on your eyes, on your shoulder, on your breast, everywhere, everywhere . . ."

In spite of his entreaties, Josephine had no wish to leave Paris, her customary activities and pleasures—and her latest lover, a young captain called Hippolyte Charles, whom she had nicknamed "my Pulchinello"; he was both a business partner and a bedmate, and in this twofold capacity seemed far more competent than Bonaparte. Playing for time, Josephine wrote her husband that she was pregnant and he cried out his joy; "I am dying to see how you bear children. It must give you a superb and majestic mien which must be very pleasant to behold." However, Josephine was soon at her wit's end and she knew she could not postpone her departure much longer. From Italy, Bonaparte was summoning the help of his brothers, his friends, and even cabinet ministers, threatening to give up his career, his army and his conquests, and rush back to his wife. The government ordered Josephine to leave for Italy without delay; but when she set off, Hippolyte was at her side, and later on, in the Italian palazzi where she held court, her "Pulchinello" hopped back into her bed each time her husband left it to win a new victory.

During the next two years, this demented passion never left Bonaparte—two long years in which he tried desperately to win his wife's love, blind to her unfaithfulness, her wiles and her cupidity. He was in Egypt when the cast fell at last from his eyes, as friends reported to him in detail Josephine's infidelities. "The veil is now torn away," he wrote his older brother Joseph, and he swore to repudiate his wife as soon as he would be back in Paris: "A divorce! Yes, a divorce! I'll expose her publicly . . . I know everything!"

Meanwhile, he endeavoured spitefully to avenge his misfortune, first with Circassian women taken over from the Mameluks (but he soon tired of their "misshapen obesity"), then with the wife of one of his general officers, and finally with a young fair-haired girl he had noticed in Cairo. He directly undertook to seduce her, and he conquered her as if she were an enemy stronghold—confusing, in his mind, as it were, love and war as alternate forms of physical and mental detumescence.

Pauline Fourès, a twenty-year-old milliner from the South of France, had donned the garb of a soldier to accompany her husband, a lieutenant in the French Expeditionary Force, to the Egyptian front. Harbouring no qualms, Bonaparte sent Fourès off on a mission to clear the way (the lieutenant was captured at sea by the British Navy and, when the finer points of his mission were revealed by Egyptian spies, the English waggishly proceeded to send him back to Alexandria). In the meantime, Bonaparte asked Pauline to dinner, where in front of his other guests he deliberately spilled a wine decanter over her dress and then, under the pretence of remedying the damage, he led her to the next room, untroubled by the snickerings of his guests, and fell headlong upon his prey.

Young, easy-going and loving, Pauline was a welcome change from Josephine. Bonaparte soon became infatuated and he kept her openly by his side. According to his secretary Bourrienne, he even went as far as promising to marry her if she bore him the child his own wife could not or would not give him. "Bonaparte was earnestly anxious to have a child by this pretty girl," wrote Bourrienne in his *Memoirs*. "One day, we discussed it at lunch. 'Well, what can I do?' he replied. 'The little fool doesn't seem to be able to give me one!' And she, for her part, when she was made to realize that bearing a child to Bonaparte would make her fortune, replied: 'Why, I'm not the one to blame!' "

Some time later, when Josephine learned that Bonaparte was coming back with the intention of divorcing her, she left Paris post-haste in an effort to intercept him on the way from Toulon, and thus win him back to her. Unfortunately, she had picked the Burgundy route while her husband had taken another road so that when she returned to Paris he had already been back for nearly three days. It was late evening when she arrived, and he had locked himself up in his room after instructing the servants not to let her in. Beset by the fear of losing her husband at the height of his career, Josephine beseeched him for hours behind the closed door. Finally, unable to hold out any longer, Bonaparte opened the door, his face drenched with tears, and took her in his arms.

Next morning, his brother Lucien found him in bed with Josephine at his side, "painted, smiling and triumphant." Once again, Bonaparte had yielded to her skilful love-making. From then on, however, the wild, tortured passion of yore gave way to an all too lucid affection and a sharp sense of reality. In fact, as he was plotting to seize power, Josephine's influence in government circles was more precious than ever to him, and he knew the time had not come to

Bonaparte and Josephine.

break away from her. Yet, their married life underwent a drastic change. Josephine was now obviously trying to make up for her wrongs, although she was still betraying him occasionally with other men. But Bonaparte was deeply wounded and disillusioned, and he deliberately shut his mind to all romantic implications about love. Shedding his masochistic docility, he began to show a deep-felt misogyny. Henceforth, love was nothing more to him than "sofa business"—a plain and inconsequential sexual urge.

In the following months, after the *coup d' Etat* which made him one of the three Consuls governing the country, he became aware of his "duties" as a public figure. He ruled out of the Tuileries the "scandal-mongering harlots" of the Directoire days, cursing the corruption of lecherous politicians as well as the "dreadfully indecent ways of women," who "exhibited themselves practically in the nude." Further still, as if haunted by his failure with Josephine, he ordered the jurists to include in the new Civil Code "the bride's duty of obedience" in the section devoted to marriage.

At the time, Bonaparte was only thirty years old. "He is short in stature," wrote Mme de Rémusat, "and rather badly proportioned, for the upper part of his body is too long and the lower part seems consequently shorter. His hair is brown and rather sparse, his eyes are greyish blue; his complexion was yellowish when he was young, and later became wan and almost colourless . . . His mien causes him to lean forward a little. When he is calm, his eyes have a melancholy and thoughtful expression, but when he is angry, his gaze becomes fierce and threatening. Laughter suits him and there is a kind of seduction in his smile . . . but during the time I knew him he did not smile often. Seriousness was his basic trait; a seriousness not born of true aristocracy of birth and behaviour, but born of deep meditations. In his youth, he was ever day-dreaming; later, he appeared to become sad, and later still this sadness turned into an almost constant bad temper . . ."

On the outside he was the bad man of Europe, a genial and self-possessed strategist, a leader of men, endowed with true hypnotic powers which literally fascinated and terrorized his friends as well as his enemies. Inside, he was a maze of weaknesses, fears and contradictions: generous to an extreme, still he sordidly noted the price paid for each gift he made; showing infinite patience, he would suddenly fly into a rage over trifles. He was, as Barras said, "in the grip of a perpetual brain-fever," and his eyes were "often drowned in tears." In a matter of seconds, from a standing start, he could throw himself into such fits of temper that he would writhe on the ground in seemingly epileptic convulsions; or often, when absorbed in thought, he would grab a penknife and mechanically lacerate the stuffing of his chair, and even his own clothes. This intensely neurotic aspect of the Emperor's character was vividly chronicled by his coachman, Jean Horn: "In moments of deep preoccupation, when a penknife happened to be at hand, he would cut into shreds his dress or the covering of the chair he was sitting on. The cloak he wore during the Russian retreat still shows proof of this imperial mania."

He seldom slept more than three hours a night, and he was capable of dropping off to sleep at will, whatever the time or place, and even in the midst of gunfire. He ate very little, no matter what, and with a repulsive voraciousness swallowing his food in a few hurried bites. He was fastidiously clean, bathed every day, cared lovingly for his hands and nails, brushed his teeth twice a day, rinsing his mouth with water laced with brandy. He had exceptional powers of concentration and worked close to twenty hours every day, dividing the rest of his time between rest and pleasure.

From the dawn of the century until Waterloo, during fifteen years,

Bonaparte kept up this schedule, although he devoted more and more time to women. However, he later said to General Gourgaud: "I never ran after women. I had other concerns. What would have become of a twenty-five-year-old commander-in-chief if he had spent his time chasing the fair sex?" This was to be his golden rule after the first two years of his life with Josephine. Then, as he climbed the rungs of fame, women became even less of a problem to him; for they no longer waited to be chased but simply threw themselves at his feet —and he took hurried advantage of them without any unnecessary sweet-talk, and, more often than not, without tomorrows.

All his mistresses were eventually abandoned—after one night or one month, some with a word of thanks, others simply thrown out the door —but, strangely enough, nearly all of them were rewarded in one way or another. Caroline du Colombier became a maid-of-honour, Félicité Turreau was offered a pension, Pauline Fourès was given in marriage to a Count of the Empire, Désirée Clary married General Bernadotte and later became Queen of Sweden ("'Tis because I took her cherry that I made him a Field-Marshall," Napoleon said to Bertrand at Saint Helena).

He did not bother to woo the women he coveted, finding it far simpler to have them summoned to the Tuileries by one of his aides-de-camp; he made love to them hurriedly, brutally, perfectly indifferent to his partners' own pleasures. His taste was eclectic and remarkably undiscriminating; depending on the day's luck, he would go from blonde to brunette, from scullion to princess, from married woman to kept actress. A great admirer of *bel canto,* he had an affair with Italy's number one *prima donna,* la Grassini, who had made passes at him during the first Italian campaign; but his love for Josephine was all-exclusive at the time and he had turned her down. In 1800, however, when he crossed the Alps again, he reminded signora Grassini of her three-year-old offer and he won the day. Upon his return to France, he asked her to come to Paris and, for several months, she was called two or three times a week to his private apartments at the Tuileries—while Josephine calmly shrugged her shoulders, knowing the *prima donna* would not last long and could in no way endanger her own position.

After the singer came an actress, Mlle George, who had just turned sixteen although she was already fantastically developed and had, in

Bonaparte's own words, a "fine smutty body!" Years later, the actress related with a wealth of details her love affair with the First Consul. "He was," she wrote smugly, "an infinitely delicate and assiduous lover . . . The first night, he yielded to my prayers and did not touch me." According to her, it was only on her third visit that she gave in to him. "During the first two weeks, he was at pains to satisfy every wish commanded by my innocence and, I dare say, my modesty—himself repairing the night's disorder and tidying the bed. He helped me wash, dress and put on my shoes; better still, as I wore garters with buckles, which taxed his impatience, he had special garters made for me, of the kind that were drawn over the feet . . ."

Bonaparte had her brought in to the Tuileries several times a week and, strangely, he behaved with her rather like a prankish schoolboy than a demanding lover. They played hide-and-seek in his study, chasing each other and falling over one another with yells of glee. "He loved to play with me," Mlle George wrote. "He would make me run after him. Then, to escape me, he would climb on the library ladder, and I would push him and laugh and call to him . . ."

Late one night, as he was in bed with her, Bonaparte was struck with a fit of delirium—whether it was epilepsy or a bout of fever caused by overwork was never known—and towards two o'clock in the morning, he suddenly lost consciousness. The terrified girl uttered piercing screams, waking up the whole palace—and Josephine herself. The scandal could not be hushed (the *émigrés* in London were to make capital out of the so-called "orgies of the mad Corsican ogre") and Mlle George was immediately dismissed from Napoleon's private parties.

Nevertheless, he kept a marked predilection for actresses—women of the world, as easy to get as they were to leave. There was Mlle Duchesnois, who competed for a while with "Georgina" on the stage as well as in Bonaparte's bed; but he never showed her the affectionate consideration which he had displayed towards his "little playmate." One night, as he had summoned her to the Tuileries, he sat down at his table to work on some reports while waiting for her. He soon was so engrossed in his work that he forgot his tryst. After some time, his valet Constant, who devotedly aided and abetted his nightly frolics, came to the door: "Mlle Duchesnois has arrived," he said. "Have her wait," answered

The Empress Josephine.   **Désirée Clary.**
Mademoiselle George.   **Pauline Bonaparte.**

Bonaparte without raising his head. An hour later, Constant came back.

"Tell her to undress," the Consul ordered. The girl was taken to his room, and she shed her clothes, slipped into bed and waited for her lover. Dawn was near when Constant, as he wrote the story later, came again to rap at his master's door. "Bah!" said Bonaparte. "Tell her to go."

Then there was another singer, la Branchu, and another actress, Mlle Bourgoing, whom he stole from one of his own cabinet ministers. He was as rude to her as he had been to Mlle Duchesnois. Late one night, after she had been waiting for several hours, she greeted him with such nagging remarks that he came fuming to the bed, pulled up the sheet and stared at her naked body with an icy gaze —then with a shrug he walked out of the room, saying: "Is that all? Well, hags like you shouldn't put up such airs!"

These are but a few examples of his customary boorishness towards women—which was perhaps one way for making them pay for his own hidden weaknesses and short-comings. He was even ruder to Josephine, scorning and reviling her in public, making base jokes about her aging looks and her sterility. One day at Malmaison, as he had

Maria Walewska.

Marie-Louise of Austria.

decided to go hunting in the park, she got up and said: "You're out of your mind, Bonaparte, it's the mating season." Gesturing wildly, he turned to the hypnotized guests and sneered: "Well, gentlemen, we must give it up. Everybody here seems to be prolific except my wife!"

Josephine was then forty years of age, and Bonaparte was haunted by the thought of her sterility. In 1804, as he was preparing to accede to the throne, he was more anxious than ever to have a direct heir. Knowing the importance of the stakes, Josephine consulted the best doctors in France and underwent scores of treatments and cures, striving desperately to regain her youth and her fecundity. One morning, as he came to a cabinet meeting, Bonaparte cried triumphantly: "My wife is menstruating again!" But his hopes were soon dampened, and even Josephine knew she could never again bear children. To turn the tables, she accused Bonaparte of being impotent, viciously adding that the two children she had given her first husband proved her own fecundity. It took Bonaparte several years to dispel the doubts she had cast in him pertaining to his virility.

Josephine, however, was crowned by his side in December, 1804. From then on he became more faithless to her than ever. According to Mme de Rémusat, her "scènes de ménage" were met "with contemptible violence and scorn, until his latest fantasy would vanish and his affection for her suddenly come back to life."

Napoleon I was infinitely more demanding than Bonaparte, more violent and erratic in his desires. Larrey, one of the best military surgeons of the time, related that one evening the Emperor returned from the battlefield "with fiery eyes, yelling: 'A woman! A woman! Immediately . . . Someone bring me a woman!' A fine time it was to think of this while wounded soldiers were dying by the thousands all around him." His was a primitive, almost bestial need, and he despised women for their inability to satisfy more than that need. At the same time, he feared and despised intelligent women—"Women should knit!" he said. Mme de Staël, who was a "femme d'esprit" and a well-known writer, was banished from Paris. Countess Caffarelli, who had dared refuse to go to bed with him, was dismissed from the Tuileries.

When Napoleon failed to seduce a woman, he made her pay dearly for it with methodical and merciless cruelty. "It is a great mistake," he told Las Cases at Saint Helena, "to have raised women to a level almost equal to ours . . . Woman was given to Man that she might bear children. Now, for this purpose, one woman cannot suffice a man, for she cannot be a wife while she is pregnant; nor can she be a wife when she gives suck or when she is ill; and she ceases to be a wife when she is no longer capable of giving birth to children." Thus he explained and justified *a posteriori* his unfaithfulness to Josephine.

At Fontainebleau, to cut short his wife's complaints, he had the hallway between their apartments sealed up. The Empress, after accusing him of impotency and sterility, and caring little to be contradicted in her own assertions, now began accusing him of having seduced her daughter, Hortense. Several years later, she told the Governor of Geneva that "the Emperor had been Hortense's lover" but upon learning that she was pregnant, he had forced his own brother, Louis, to marry her. In like manner, Josephine deliberately spread the rumour that Napoleon had tried to rape his youngest brother Jérome's fiancée.' (Much has been said about Napoleon's incestuous love affairs with Stéphanie de Beauharnais, Josephine's niece, and even with his own sisters Caroline and Pauline. Many pamphlets, written by royalist *émigrés*, supported the accusations and added rather dubious "testimonies" of their own. However, these assertions seem to be based on shaky arguments; in point of fact, Napoleon had an acute sense of his responsibilities towards his family, and, for that matter, neither he nor his sisters had ever lacked for bedmates.)

At the age of thirty-five, when he acceded to the throne, his fits of morbid nervousness were rarer but far more violent. With his mistresses, he was as exacting, hurried and cruel as ever. He hated perfumes and it was commonly known that he might well throw a woman out of his bed if he detected any "foreign scent." One day, in Saint Helena, as he was recalling a woman he had slept with in Vienna in 1805, he told Gourgaud: "She was one of the most pleasant women I have ever known: not the least bodily odour!"

After his coronation, he began nominating ladies-in-waiting and maids-of-honour, thus making it easier for himself to seduce the women who attracted his fancy. There was Mme Duchâtel, who was the most discreet and devoted of his mistresses; there were the Demoiselles Lacoste and Guillebeau, and Mme Gazzani, whom he had appointed as Court readers. Then came Eléonore Denuelle de la Plaigne who was lady-in-waiting to his sister Caroline. She was a tall girl of nineteen, with jay-black eyes, a cool head, and a compliant body. As soon as he noticed her, Napoleon became infatuated. He had her summoned to his apartments and took her directly to task. She submitted readily and soon became a steady visitor, feigning a passion she hardly felt and exerting her wiles to bind her imperial lover to her. Later, she herself related that when she was called to the Emperor's rooms she would often surreptitiously move the hands of the clock forward; Napoleon would come, tumble into bed with her, then looking at the time he would say, "Already!", give her a quick peck on the cheek, and hurry back to his study.

After a few weeks, Eléonore told him she was pregnant and Napoleon jumped with joy as he realized that he was giving the lie to Josephine's accusations. In late December, 1806, in the house he had given her on Rue de la Victoire—near the hotel Chantereine where he had spent his first months with Josephine — Eléonore gave birth to a boy who was christened Léon, "son of Miss E. Denuelle and of *absent* father."

When the Emperor learned of the birth of his first child, he was on the Polish border. And the next day, on the road to Warsaw, he met a woman who was to play an important part in his political as well as his personal life. Maria Walewska was a fair, slim and ardent girl in her early twenties, married to a gouty Polish count. A fanatic patriot, she looked up to Napoleon as the liberator of her country, which had been under Russian rule for the past eleven years—and, as the Emperor's coach went by, she threw him a posy of flowers.

Dazzled by this Polish Passionaria, Napoleon inquired about her and had her invited to the ball which was to be given in his honour in Warsaw. When she came, he tried to seduce her in the same way as the women of the Tuileries, but Maria was so innocent and chaste that she did not even understand the quite unequivocal implications of Napoleon's pressing words. As she returned home after the ball, she found a note which had just been brought by an aide:

"I have seen only you, it is you only I have admired, it is you only I desire. A prompt reply to calm the impatient fervour of

N."

Horrified, Maria had the messenger thrown out. This unexpected resistance teased Napoleon's fancy, and his crude and potent urge grew overnight into a violent passion. "The morning after the ball," wrote his valet Constant, "he kept getting up, walking about, sitting down and getting up again. I thought I would never be able to help him dress." That same morning, as Maria woke up, a messenger brought another message which was hardly less pressing and uncouth than the first:

"Have I displeased you, Madam? Yet I felt justified in hoping for the contrary. Have I been mistaken? Your eagerness declines while mine grows all the more. You bereave me of my peace of mind. Oh, won't you give a little joy and happiness to a poor heart ready to worship you. Is a reply so difficult to obtain? You owe me two.

N."

Maria sent the message back unopened. All day long, emissaries and ambassadors thronged round her waiting-room, trying to convince her, "for the love of Poland," to surrender to the Emperor's desires. Finally, the Warsaw bigwigs, frightened at the thought of Napoleon's displeasure, joined forces against the rebel and sent her this bombastic and insane plea:

"Madam, women throughout the ages have had a great influence on

The arcades of Palais-Royal.

the world's politics. If you had been a man, you would have readily given your life for the worthy and just cause of the Fatherland. As a woman, there are other sacrifices which you can make and must impose upon yourself—even if they are painful to you. Do you think Esther yielded to Assuerus out of love? No, she sacrificed herself to save her country and she has had the glorious honour of having succeeded. Would that we might say the same for your glory and our salvation."

Beset from all sides, Maria finally gave in and promised to yield to

65

the Corsican Assuerus. "Oh, do come, do come," implored Napoleon in a third note. "All your wishes shall be fulfilled. Your Fatherland will be dearer to me if you have pity on my poor heart."

Maria was prepared for the sacrifice, and that very evening she was led to the Palace and into the small badly-lit drawing-room. The Emperor soon arrived and threw himself at her knees. Suddenly, he took her in his arms and tried to steal a kiss. Pushing him away, Maria jumped up and ran for the door, but he reached it before her and forced her back to her seat. Still, he was moved by her tears and, controlling his impatience, was again for a moment the shy, sentimental and submissive boy of his youth. That night, Maria went home unmolested. The next morning, a messenger brought her a bunch of laurel with a diamond necklace and yet another message hidden within. The note read: "Maria, my sweet Maria, my first thought is for you, my first wish is to see you again. You will come back, won't you? You gave me your promise. Otherwise, the eagle will fly to you . . ."

Throwing the jewels away, Maria determined to flee Warsaw—then she changed her mind and dutifully came to the night's tryst. When she arrived, Napoleon had lost his tender patience of the night before, and he threatened her with the arguments of a petty blackmailer. "I will force you to love me," he said. "I have brought your country back to life. But take heed! Like this watch which I hold in my hand and break before your eyes—so will the name of Poland vanish if you tax my patience and refuse me your heart."

Saying this, he threw the watch on the floor. Maria fainted. When she came to, he was kneeling by her side and he made it clear by his attitude that he had abused her while she was unconscious. There again, had he had a fit of delirium or epilepsy as has been suggested by several historians? It is impossible to say. Be it as it may, he could not repress his urge . . . Still half-unconscious, Maria was carried into the apartment which had been prepared for her in the Emperor's palace.

During the next few weeks, she was shut up from the outside world. She saw only him, talked only with him and, gradually, the repulsion of the first day gave way to comprehension, then affection and eventually to love. She left her husband to remain by Napoleon's side—even when she realized he was already betraying his promise

66

to re-establish Poland's independence. She followed him to Paris, then to Vienna—and soon, for the second time, Napoleon had a son. It was apparently at this moment that he resolved to repudiate Josephine, even though he knew that he could never marry Maria.

Upon his return to Paris, one November evening in 1809, he announced his decision to Josephine and, as she was bursting into tears, he made this strange comment: "Do you know that this divorce will be an important episode in my life? What a scene it would make in a tragedy!" Oddly, as soon as this "episode" was accomplished, Napoleon nearly fell back in love with Josephine, a love mingled with compassion and self-pity at the memory of his past happiness. For a few months, he often visited her at Malmaison, sending her loving and nostalgic letters, going to great pains to console her with jewels, property and money. "She alone has been the companion of my life," he told Champagny. "Only reasons of State could force me to marry again, but then I would marry a womb."

Actually, he was already looking for another bride, and his choice fell on the Archduchess Marie-Louise, daughter of the Emperor of Austria and niece of Marie-Antoinette. She was a plump girl of nineteen, gluttonous, stupid and obscurely sensual. Although she had grown up under the constant fear of the "Corsican ogre," she readily accepted the match and soon, Marshal Berthier, an all-time comrade of Napoleon's, arrived in Vienna to take her to her future husband.

Napoleon had already forgotten Josephine, Maria Walewska and all the women who had crossed his path. Eaten away by impatience and anxiety, he even seemed to forget the existence of his two sons and was again haunted by the obsession of sterility. Corvisart, the Court doctor and a close confidant of the Emperor, later reported a conversation he had had with him at the time:

"What is the average duration of potency with regard to paternity?" Napoleon asked him. "For instance, is it still possible for a man of sixty to have children with a young girl?"

"Sometimes."

"And for a man of seventy?"

"Always, Majesty," laughed the doctor.

Napoleon, who had just turned forty, felt his confidence soar again. As he was waiting for Marie-Louise, he plied with childish and quite obscene questions those who had approached her at the Viennese

Court. Anxious to please his royal bride he had his wardrobe refurnished and even took dancing lessons with Hortense and Stéphanie de Beauharnais.

The Archduchess and her retinue were due to arrive at Soissons on the 27th of March 1810. That day, unable to restrain himself any longer, Napoleon got up at dawn, ordered a coach with no armorial bearings and rushed on the road to meet her. Jumping from his seat, he stopped her carriage, opened the door and climbed inside. Marie-Louise, who was suffering from a head cold, had a red nose, weeping eyes and a hoarse voice which aggravated her strong German accent. With drawn curtains, the coach went past the Soissons stage and did not stop until Compiègne. When Napoleon climbed out, his triumphant face allowed little doubt as to the reasons for this change of plans. Cutting short the speeches of the Compiègne dignitaries, he immediately led Marie-Louise to the apartment which had been prepared for her and, brushing protocol away, he would not hear of leaving her for the night.

In point of fact, he raped the "daughter of the Cæsars" as a frontline trooper would abuse a common stable-maid, with none of the tact and regard he had shown towards Mlle George. Next morning, smiling and relaxed, he asked Constant "if anyone at Court had noticed the slight dent he had made in the programme," then, as an officer entered his room, he welcomed him with an even broader smile and exclaimed: "My boy, you should marry a German girl. They are the best in the world, sweet, innocent and fresh as roses."

He stayed all day with Marie-Louise—and she hardly left her room. Brutally as she had been initiated, she did not seem unhappy about it, and she soon proved to be so greedy and demanding that, on Corvisart's advice, her husband had to ask for mercy.

In the first few weeks after the official wedding, Napoleon was her ready slave. He would interrupt audiences and cabinet meetings to jump into her bed, forsaking his duties for hours on end. "He loves her so obviously that he cannot hide his feelings," Metternich reported to his master, the Emperor of Austria. "Everything is now deferred to his desires." Napoleon showered jewels and gifts of all kinds upon Marie-Louise, who once made this gaudy comment: "My, the Emperor keeps his women well!"

His happiness soon turned into bliss when the long-awaited heir was born. But the situation degenerated rapidly. Marie-Louise had little love for her husband, and as soon as his throne began to founder she deserted him without qualms—before openly betraying the fallen Master of Europe in the arms of a one-eyed Austrian nobleman. Napoleon saw her and his son for the last time, shortly before his exile to Elba—and while he reigned on this minute rock, abandoned by his friends, and even his family, the only woman to remain faithful to him was Maria Walewska.

At Elba, Napoleon's love-life dwindled considerably. He had a few superficial affairs, either with female visitors from Paris, or, in keeping with his life-long habits, with the wives of local dignitaries. Physically, he appeared tired and weakened—and, in his own words at the time, "detached from love." After Easter Sunday, 1815, and his return to Paris for the last hundred days of his reign, he made somewhat absent-minded passes at a few old-timers: Mme Duchatel, Mlle George, and again Maria—who after the disaster of Waterloo and the collapse of the Empire, offered in vain to accompany him to Saint Helena.

On this tiny and desolate island he was to spend the last six years of his life, dictating his memoirs and reminiscing the past. He had a last desultory affair with Countess Montholon, but he soon gave it up. "My dear boy," he said one day to her husband, "when a man is fifty and as worn out as I am, it is hardly worthwhile to dream of women.'

Nevertheless, he was still dreaming of them. Time and again, he would conjure up his old loves and proudly unfold before Gourgaud some of the crudest episodes of his love-life, raving for hours on end, comparing with senile shamelessness the finer points of his mistresses, as well as of his two wives—the Creole skills of Josephine and Marie-Louise's Teutonic eagerness.

At fifty, he was already an old man, puffed up, exhausted, eaten away by his short-lived career. After his death on the 5th of May, 1821, Major Henry, a military surgeon who was present at the autopsy, noted the almost total disappearance of hairs, and the minute, atrophied proportions of the Emperor's heart and genital parts—*"exiguitatis insignis, sicut pueri . . ."* This might explain partially Napoleon's behaviour towards women—as if he had always been striving to hide some strange masochistic fear behind a mask of cynical and uncouth recklessness. He was an avid lover but hardly a connoisseur;

selfish and demanding, he was doubtlessly prone to occasional failings of virility—and his sexual urges were too brutally and quickly gratified not to induce in him a form of misogyny.

"Yet you must not think that I don't have as sensitive a heart as other men," he once said to Molé, his Minister of Justice. "But I have always endeavoured to mute this string. Thus, were I told in the midst of a battle that my mistress, over whom I am losing my head, has just breathed her last, it would not affect me in the least." Surely he needed women and even loved a few of them to a point, but he had no respect for them—nor, for that matter, for love itself. He once threw out of the Tuileries an over-eager and covetous mistress, Mme de Vaudey, saying: "I have neither enough gold nor enough heart to pay such a high price for something which can be had so cheap."

Thus lived Josephine's lover and Marie-Louise's conqueror—a soldier far more at ease on the battlefield than in love's alcoves—a man who was so deeply convinced of the uniqueness of his career, that as he was nearing the end of his life, he felt that the "sheer purity of his glory" had only been sullied by the "gross complications" of sex.

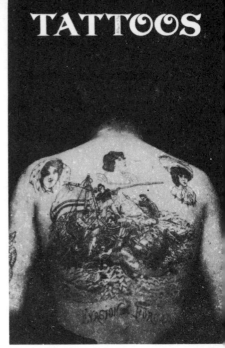

The superb *Evasion de Forcats* shows a group of prisoners escaping on a raft from the convict camp of Saint-Laurent-du-Maroni in French Guiana.

THE SKIN ARTISTS
Photographs from the collection of Robert Giraud

Long days spent in jail, or in the disciplinary units of the army in Africa (the *Bat' d'Af'* or *Battaillons d'Afrique*), encouraged the vogue of tattooing among French *truands* (toughs).

Engraving indelible figures under the skin is not a new practice—nor was it always confined to social outlaws. It was in favour among

British aristocrats at the close of the XIXth century. One century earlier, Bernadotte, a soldier of the French revolution and one of Napoleon's earlier companions, was unable to erase from his right arm, after he acceded to the throne of Sweden, the revolutionary motto of his youth: "Death to the Kings".

Apart from rare exceptions (Frederik of Denmark is the last king to sport Chinese dragons on his biceps), the tradition is now practically extinct in either good or bad society. The examples shown in these pages were modelled by denizens of the French underworld; they date back from before World War I and could hardly be duplicated today: contemporary gangsters prefer an unidentifiable skin to this form of candid self-glorification.

Tattooing can be either descriptive or symbolic. The prison artists have adorned the skin of their cellmates with portraits and scenes which are sometimes very elaborate —or with allegories representing a man's character, past experiences or speciality in thugdom.

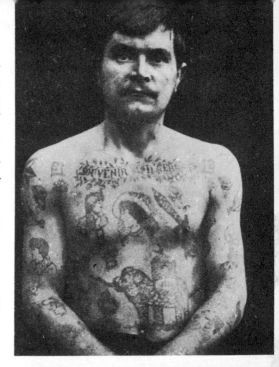

African landscapes are to be found on many chests and shoulder blades, reminiscent of years spent under the violent sun of hard labour, and portraits—usually of lost mistresses and nostalgic mothers.

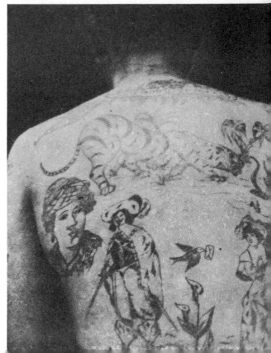

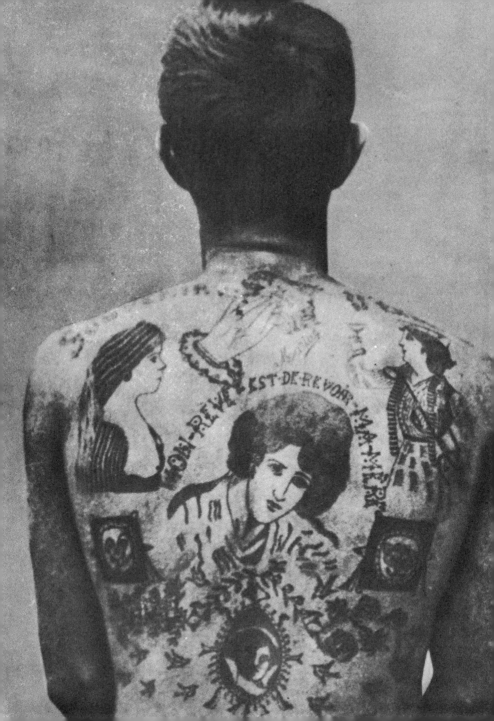

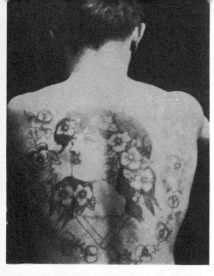

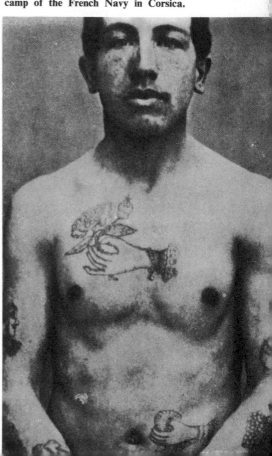

Left: An image of romantic passion.

The young man below proclaims his dedication to Greek love by means of a rose placed on his heart; lower down, a hand manipulating his bowels reveals his fine sensitive nature; and the bunch of grapes on his right arm tells us that he has served time in a disciplinary camp of the French Navy in Corsica.

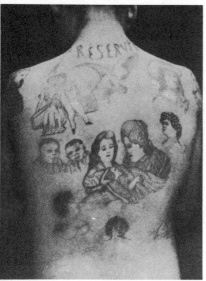

The eagle carrying a woman away is a label of the pimps—and the word "Réservé" written across the neck is meant to help the executioner find the suitable place when comes the time of the guillotine.

The Maudlin character on the left declares that his dream is to see his mother once more.

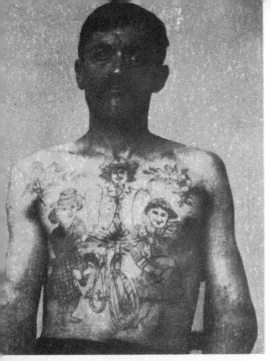

The ruddy-faced, moustachioed individual on the left probably wanted to record on his own skin one great moment of his life—when two elegant sportswomen taught him how to ride a bicycle in unconstrained Douanier-Rousseau-like fashion.

The individual just below divided his attention between precious doe-eyed females and political figures of his day—prosperous-looking Fathers of the Third Republic.

As to the man on the right, he does not entertain any great hopes for the future. The inscription, "Martyr Militaire", shows him as belonging to either the Bat' d'Af' or the Foreign Legion. The guillotine occupies the central place in that composition, an ominous symbol of the inescapable fate which awaits that victim of bad luck and misery; the executioner and priest, both in full regalia, flank the sinister mechanism, and the face of the unfortunate one is seen peering through the head-hole prior to dropping into the basket of eternity.

The guillotine is only one of the many recurrent symbols used in tattooing. Others are: the Tiger (brute strength); the Lion (manly courage); d'Artagnan-the-Musketeer (swagger and bravado); the Clown ("I laugh at everything"); the Swallows ("Good news is expected").

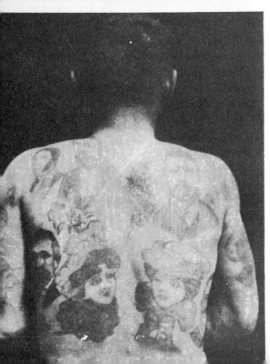

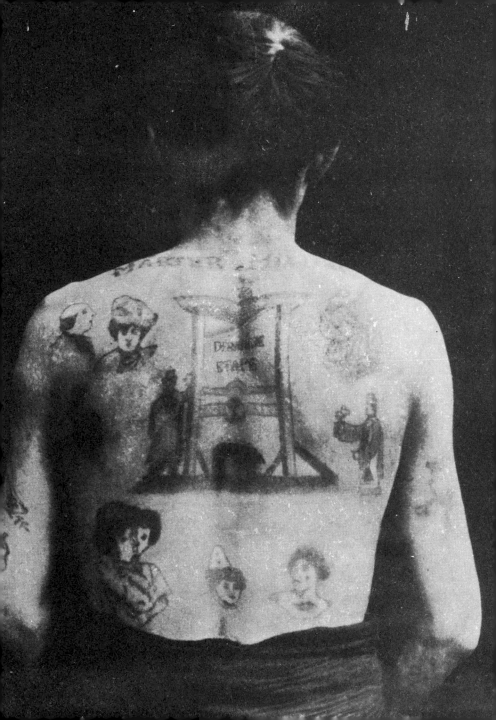

1601
by MARK TWAIN

Although the authorship of 1601 *was never officially established, there can be no doubt that Mark Twain wrote that wonderful* pastiche *of Elizabethan prose in* 1876, *or shortly thereafter. In his biography, Albert Bigelow Paine notes that Mark Twain took a particular delight in reading Pepy's Diary during that period, and was thus encouraged to write this* Fireside Conversation in the Time of Queen Elizabeth— *which title was later changed to* 1601. *Paine adds: "It was written as a letter to that robust divine, Reverend Joseph Twitchell, who had no special scruples concerning Shakespearian parlance and customs."*

In this same biography, a passage from one of Mark Twain's note-books of a later period is reproduced, which leaves no doubt as to the authorship of 1601: *"It depends on who writes a thing whether it is coarse or not. I once wrote a conversation between Elizabeth, Shakespeare, Ben Johnson, Beaumont, Sir Walter Raleigh, Lord Bacon, Sir Nicholas Throckmorton, and a stupid old nobleman—this latter being cup-bearer to the queen and ostensible reporter of the talk.*

"There were four maids of honour present and a sweet young girl two years younger than the boy Beaumont. I built a conversation which could *have happened—I used words such as* were *used at that time—*1601. *I sent it anonymously to a magazine, and how the editor abused it and the sender. But that man was a praiser of Rabelais, and had been saying, 'O that we had a Rabelais.' I judged I could furnish him one."*

But Rabelais' colourful vocabulary was acceptable in the XVIth century, as was Shapespeare's in the XVIIth. Had those two lived in the XIXth century, or even the XXth century, they would no doubt have been persecuted by the Bowdlers of the time. Such was the fate of Mark Twain—at least insofar as this little piece of elegant mischief was concerned.

John Hay, who had seen the manuscript of 1601 *and praised it highly, surreptitiously permitted copies to be made, which were in turn reproduced in a few privately printed editions, released at different times.*

This is the first "official" publication of 1601. *To see it in print is enough to measure the inanity of Victorian censorship, and to wonder at the witlessness of those stout moralists who, to this day, have prevented such a charming masterpiece as this to pursue its career in the open.*

(Mem.—The following is supposed to be an extract from the diary of the Pepys of that day, the same being cupbearer to Queen Elizabeth. It is supposed that he is of ancient and noble lineage; that he despises these canaille; that his soul consumes with wrath to see the Queen stooping to talk to such; and that the old man feels his nobility defiled by contact with Shakespeare, etc., and yet he has got to stay there till Her Majesty chooses to dismiss him.)

Illustrations by Norman Rubington.

Yesternight took her Majestie, ye Queene, a fantasie such as she sometimes hath, and hadde to her closet certain that do write playes, bookes and such like—these being my Lord Bacon, his worship, Sir Walter Ralegh, Mr. Ben Jonson, and ye childe Francis Beaumont, which being but sixteen hath yet turned his hande to ye doing of ye Latin masters into our English tongue with great discretion and much applause. Also came with those ye famous Shaxpur. A right strange mingling of mightie blood with meane, ye more in especial since ye Queene's Grace was present as likewise these following, to wit: Ye Duchesse of Bilgewater, twenty-two years of age; ye Countess of Granby thirty-six; her dotor, ye Lady Helen; as also ye two maides of honour, to wit: Ye Lady Margery Bothby, sixty-five; ye Lady Alice Dilbury, turned seventy, she being two yeares ye Queene's Grace's elder.

I, being Her Majestie's cupbearer, had no choice but to remain and behold rank forgot, and ye high hold converse with ye low as upon equal termes, and a great scandal did ye world heare thereof.

In ye heate of ye talke, it befel that one did breake wynde, yielding an exceeding mightie and distressful stinke, whereat all did laffe full sore, and then:

77

YE QUEENE: Verily, in mine eight and sixty yeares have I not hearde ye fellow to this fartte. Meseemeth by ye greate sound and clamour of it, it was male yet ye bellie it did lurke behinde should now falle lene and flat against ye spine of him that hath been delivered of so stately and so vaste a bulke, whereas ye guts of them that doe quiff-splitters beare, stand comely, stille and rounde. Prithee, let ye author confess ye offspring. Will my Lady Alice testify?

LADY ALICE: Goode your Grace, an' I hadde roome for such a thundergust within mine ancient bowels, 'tis not in reason I could discharge the same and live to thank God for that he did chuse hand-mayd so humble to show his power. Nay, 'tis not I that have brought forth this rich o'ermastering fog, this fragrant gloom, so pray seek ye further.

YE QUEENE: Mayhap ye Lady Margery hath done ye companie this favour?

LADY MARGERY: So please you, Madame, my limbs are feeble with ye weighte and drouthe of five and sixty winters, and it behooveth that I be tender with them. In ye goode providence of God, an' hadde I contained this wonder forsooth would I have given ye whole evening of my sinking life to ye dribbling of it forthe with trembling and uneasy soul, not launched it sudden in its matchless might, taking my own life with violence, rending my weake frame like rotten rags. It was not I, your Majestie.

YE QUEENE: In God's name who hath favoured us? Hath it come to pass that a fartte shall fartte itself? Not such a one as this I trow. Young Master Beaumont? But no, 'twould have wafted him to Heaven like down of goose's bodie. 'Twas not ye little Lady Helen,—nay, ne'er blush, my childe, thou'lt tickle thy tender maidenhedde with many a mousie squeak before thou learn'st to blow a hurricane. Was't you, my learned and ingenious Jonson?

JONSON: So felle a blast hath ne'er mine ears saluted, not yet a stenche so all-pervading and immortal. 'Twas not a novice did it, good Your Majestie, but one of veteran experience—else had he failed of confidence. In sooth it was not I.

YE QUEENE: My Lord Bacon?

LORD BACON: Not from my lene entrails hath this prodigie burst forth, so please Your Grace. Nau't doth so befit ye greate as greate performance; and haply shall ye find that 'tis not from mediocrity this miracle hath issued.

(Tho' ye subject be but a fartte, yet will this tedious sink of learning ponderously philosophize. Meantime did ye foul and deadly stinke pervade all places to that degree, that never smelt I ye like, yet dared I not leave ye Presence, albeit I was like to suffocate.)

YE QUEENE: What saith your worshipful Master Shaxpur?

SHAXPUR: In ye greate hande of God. I stande and so proclaim my innocence. Tho' ye sinless hoste of Heaven hadde fortold ye coming of this most disolating breath, proclaiming it a worke of uninspired man; its quaking thunders, its firmament-clogging rottenness his own achievement in due course of nature, yet hadde I not believed it; but hadde said, "ye Pit itself hath furnished forth ye stinke and Heaven's artillery hath shook ye globe in admiration of it."

(Then there was silence, and each did turne him toward ye worshipful Sir Walter Ralegh, that browned, embattled, bloudy swashbuckler, who rousing up did smile and simpering say):

RALEGH: Most gracious Majestie, 'twas I that did it; but, indeed, it was so poor and fragile a note compared with such as I am wont to furnish, that in sooth I was ashamed to call ye weakling mine in so august a Presence. It was nothing— less than nothing—Madame. I did it but to clear my nether throat; but hadde I come prepared then hadde I delivered something worthie. Beare with me, please your Grace, till I can make amends.

(Then delivered he himself of such a godlesse and rock-shivering blaste, that all were fain to stop their ears, and following it did come so dense and foul a stinke, that that which went before did seem a poor and trifling thing beside it . . . Then saith he, feigning that he blushed and was confused, "I perceive that I am weake today and cannot justice doe unto my powers," and sat him down as who should say,— "There, it is not much; yet he that hath an arse to spare, let him follow that, an' he think he can."

By God, an' I were ye Queene, I would e'en tip this swaggering braggard out o' ye court and let him air his grandeurs and breake his intolerable wynd before ye deaf and such as suffocation pleaseth.)

Then fell they to talk about the manners and customs of many peoples, and master Shaxpur spake of ye booke by Sir Michael Montaine, wherein was mention of ye custom of ye widows of Perigord, to wear upon ye head-dress, in sign of widowhood, a jewel in ye similitude of a man's member wilted and limber, whereat ye Queene did laffe and say, widows in England do wear prickers too, but 'twixt ye thyghs and not wilted either, till coition hath done that office for them. Master Shaxpur did also observe that the Sieur de Montaine hath also spoken of a certain emperor of such mightie prowess that he did take ten maiden-heddes in ye compass of a single night, the while his empress did entertain two and twenty lusty knights atween her sheets and yet was not satisfied; whereat ye merrie Countess Granby saith, a ram is yet ye Emperor's superior, since he will top above a hundred ewes 'twixt sun and sun, and after, if he can have none more to shag, will masturbate until he hath enryched whole acres with hys seed.

Then spake ye damned wynd-mill, Sir Walter, of a people in ye uttermost parts of America, that copulate not until they be five and thirty yeares of age, ye women being eight and twenty, and do it then but once in seven yeares.

YE QUEENE: How doth that like, my little Lady Helen? Shall we send thee thither and preserve thy belly?

LADY HELEN: Please your Highness' Grace, mine old nurse hath told me there bee more ways of serving God than by locking the thyghs together; yet I am ready to serve him in that way too, since your Highness' Grace hath set ye example.

YE QUEENE: God's woundes, a good answer, childe.

LADY ALICE: Mayhap 'twill weaken when ye hair sprouts below ye navel.

LADY HELEN: Nay, it sprouted two years since; I can scarce more than cover it with my hand now.

YE QUEENE: Heare ye that, my little Beaumont? Have you not a small birde about ye that stirs at hearing of so sweet a nest?

BEAUMONT: 'Tis not insensible, moste illustrious Madame; but mousing owls and bats of low degree may not aspire to bliss so overwhelming and ecstatic as is found in the downy nestes of birdes of Paradise.

YE QUEENE: By ye gullet of God, 'tis a neat turned compliment. With such a tongue as thyne, lad, thou'lt spread the ivorie thyghs of many a willing maide in thy goode time, an' thy codpiece be as handy as thy speech.

(Then spake ye Queene of how she met old Rabelais when she was turned fifteen, and hee did tell her of a man his father knew that hadde a double pair of bollocks, whereon a controversy followed as concerning ye moste just way to spell ye word, ye controversy running high 'twixt ye learned Bacon and ye ingenious Jonson, until at last ye olde Lady Margery, wearying of it all, saith, "Gentles, what mattereth it how ye spell ye word? I warant ye when ye use your bollocks ye shall not think of it; and my Lady Granby, bee ye content, let ye spelling be; ye shall enjoy ye beating of them on your buttocks just ye same I trow. Before I had gained my fourteenth yeare, I hadde learned that them that would explore a cunt, stopp'd not to consider ye spelling o't.")

SIR WALTER: In sooth, when a shift's turned uppe, delay is meet for naught but dalliance. Boccaccio hath a story of a priest that did beguile a mayd into his cell, then knelt him in a corner for to pray for grace that he been rightly thankful for this tender maiden-hedde the Lord hadde sent him, but the abbot spying through ye keyhole did see a tuft of brownish hair with fair white flesh about it, wherefore, when ye priest's prayer was done his chance was gone, forasmuch as ye little mayd hadde but ye one cunt and that was already occupied to her content.

Then conversed they of religion and the mightie worke ye old dead Luther did doe by ye grace of God. Then next about poetry, and Master Shaxpur did read a part of his King Henrie IV, the which it seemeth unto mee is not of the value of a arseful of ashes, yet they praised it bravely, one and all.

The same did rede a portion of his Venus and Adonis to their prodigious admiration, whereas I, being sleepy and fatigued withal, did deem it but paltry stuffe and was ye more discomfitted in that ye bloudy buccaneer hadde got wynd again and did turn his minde to farting with such villain zeal that presently I was like to choke once more. God damn this wyndy ruffian and all his breed. I would that helle might get hym.

They talked about the wonderful defense which olde Nicholas Throgmorton did make for himself before ye judges in ye time of Mary, which was unlucky matter for to broach, since it fetched out ye Queene with a pity that he, having so much wit, had yet not enough to save his daughter's maidenhedde sound for her marriage bedde, and ye Queene did give ye damned Sir Walter a look that made him wince—for she hath not forgot that he was her own lover in ye olden days. There was a silent uncomfortableness now, 'twas not a good turne for talke to take, since if ye Queene must find offense in a little harmless debauching, when prickes were stiff and cunts not loath to take the stiffness out of them, who of the company was sinless? Beholde, was not ye wife of Master Shaxpur four months gone with childe when she stood uppe before ye altar? Was not her grace of Bilgewater rogered by four lords before she had a husband?

Was not little Lady Helen born on her mother's wedding day? And beholde, were not ye Lady Alice and Lady Margery there, mouthing religion, whores from the cradle?

In time they came to discourse of Cervantes and of ye new painter Rubens, that is beginning to be heard of. Fine words and dainty wrought phrases from ye ladies now, one or two of them beeing in other days, pupils of that poore asse, Lillie, himselfe: and I marked how that Jonson and Shaxpur did fidget to discharge some venom of sarcasm, yet dared they not in ye presence, ye Queene's grace beeing ye very flower in ye Euphuists herself. But behold, there bee they that, having a specialtie and admiring it in themselves, bee jealous when a neighbor doth essay it nor can abide it in them very long.

Wherefore it was observed that ye Queene waxed uncontent; and in time a laboured grandiose speeche out of ye mouth of Lady Alice, who manifestly did mightylie pride herself thereon, did quite exhaust ye Queene's endurance, who listened til ye gaudy speeche was done, then lifting up her brows and with vaste irony, mincing, saith, "O Shit!" Whereat they all did laffe, but not ye Lady Alice, that olde foole bitche.

Now was Sir Walter minded of a tale he once did heare ye ingenious Margaret of Navarre relate about a mayd, which being like to suffer rape by an olde archbishop, did smartly contrive a device to save her maidenhedde, and said to him: "First, my Lord, prithee take out thy toole and pisse before me," which doing, Lo! his member fell and would not rise again.

AN EGYPTIAN BONDAGE
by JASCHA KESSLER

I had not gone to the movies in three years. Saturday morning my mother gave me my allowance, and off I trotted with the kids, getting as far as the Palace Delicatessen where we bolted hotdogs *with,* plates of *frenchfridays, cole-slaw,* sour pickles dipped in that special *delli* mustard, and swilled Dr. Brown's Sunray Celery Tonic. But I never bought my ticket. In the winter, I hung about the lobby, to keep warm, reading the garish coming-attractions posters, each in its glassed-in shrine lit up by hidden, coloured, 10-watt bulbs: three posters on the right, three on the left. I looked at the glossy, cornily posed stills of the current movies over and over again, and listened to the uproar of a million kids there in the darkness beyond the swinging bronzed doors. I heard their silly giggling with the zany sounding cartoons, and their hushings of each other as the creepy music that introduced the chapter came on—twenty weeks of Flash Gordon crackling and zooming and disintegrating his way through outer space, twenty weeks of Charlie Chan against the Spider Men of the Yellow Tong, twenty weeks of The Shadow pitting his hypnotic guile against the clank-ing Master Robots, twenty weeks of Tarzan hallooing his leopards and apes on the Zombie Island . . . and then the meaningless music and speech of the two feature films: agonized yells, shots, blasts of TNT, mutterings and sighing, crisp commands, screams and pleading female voices. Four long hours I mooched around there, bored to nausea, but I never went in. And in the sweltering, humid light of July and August, I used to forsake the shade of the marquee and the cool, still lobby to lope sweating back to the hide-out in our ash-heaped, weed-choked lots, gather stones for an hour and throw them steadily at the tinny billboards for the next two hours—crang crangcrung!—without stopping or breaking the beat. It was awful. And after they came out to have to listen to the grinding, point by point discussion of the show! "Remember when Dr. Zitho takes out the special needle and sticks it in his throat?" "Yow! and the water starts pouring in and he can't get out and they took Janie on the other ship and there's a time-bomb on the engine and . . ." "Suppose he shoots and he doesn't know the Black Squad loaded it with spoiled dumdums?" "Yow!" and "Yeah! Yeah!" and "Yow!"

Those years after ten are tedious; whatever helps them pass quickly is a pure gift to be grateful for. Yet if I hadn't taken to the delights of the movies, I had a good reason. It wasn't because I was saving quarters for anything, because, conscientiously, I spent them here and there, dragging out those long afternoons with candy and ice cream; and I was careful not to do anything useful, like reading the comic books my gang deposited with me out of compassion at the ticket-taker's stand. No—I was testing my will power. So, while the others rioted like eastern flowers in Californian gardens, I shrivelled in monotonous passion, petrified by the struggle between will and fierce desire which raged in renewed spasm each Saturday. Of course I did not know that the regular small victory of my ethical will snapped my foundation, bringing me that much closer to the defeat I dreaded. Being only an ungrown boy, I had no fibre to support my purpose; so that by the end of the third year I was worn out and rotten. And considering that except for the vow to resist I'd made long ago I had no reason to carry stubbornly on, how had I been able to keep it up?

My strength was derived from the last movie I had seen: *The Cat People,* a shadowy film created in the blackness of the heart. In the first of my minatory images, Simone

Simon sat in her bathroom, wearing a nightrobe which fell away from long thighs as she deftly raised a crossed leg, leaned forward and rolled the other stocking off on her cool, slim fingers; then the robe cast itself to the floor as she sank into her tub, tilted back her head of blonde curls, and dropped into a tranced sleep. Then, there was a frightened man who wore a trenchcoat; his character was obscured to me by the crush hat brimmed over his eyes as he hastened along rain-dripping wet streets: what had he done to Simone Simon? And the grand woman with the eyes of a lynx, who was she? And the woman in a fur coat, who walked through the night, flanked by a high wall of squarecut stone blocks . . . she began to scurry on her high heels, and each time she emerged into the foggy zone of a streetlamp she was terribly anxious; then there was an unearthly yowl and she ran, scared; but it was hopeless, for above her, behind her, gliding on top of the wall, was a rippling shadow—the silent, sleek, bestial power of a black panther stalking its human prey. That was what I remembered, and I was no longer certain it was at all correctly remembered; these scenes elaborated themselves infinitely in my fantasy. In reviewing their permutations and combinations when they came again and again harrowing my heart, I could not discover whether good or evil won out. Nevertheless, during my three years' continence these images gave me the meagre triumph of having kept my vow; for wretchedly puerile though they were, they suggested enough about the world. Such were the motives, they hinted, behind the doors bolted at midnight, an automatic tucked beneath a pillow or laid handy in the night-table drawer—and for the terrors of my own suffering sleep. By refraining from those delirious Saturdays of the others, I pursued purity and preserved the native innocence from which I believed the final, lasting strength might some day come. Had I not been too young for words, I could have expressed the gist of my foolish wisdom by an inspiriting motto such as, *To remain free, keep out the truth.*

Gone with the Wind broke me. As a birthday treat, my parents had me wash, dressed me in my first real suit—long pants and jacket of navy-blue serge, starched white shirt with ready-made clip-on tie of jaunty red plaid—took me into the steaming subways, dined me downtown somewhere on dead steak and dry potatoes, stood me with them for an hour or more in a line stretching clear around Rockefeller Center under the grilling August sun, and paid theatre prices for seats in the Radio City Music Hall. And I grumbled at them the whole way, fearing this exception to my record which I had let them tempt and force me into for their sake, so that they should be pleased to celebrate my birthday . . . until we were inside. The wealth of that lobby! Wurlitzer music floating like perfume in its vastitude; the mottled, creamy marbles; that piled carpeting; those braid-encrusted epauletted users, fit to be chosen for the President's Honor Guardians; and the breathing silence of thousands of people waiting rapturously in the violet air that suffused its immeasurable spaces before the film went on—that violet, premonitory glow which was neither glimmering dusk nor yet dreamful dark. Then colour, beauty and colour! Scarlett and Rhett, Ashley and Melanie: stormy love and stormful anger, melancholy torment of noble impetuosity, and the technicolored doom of Atlanta in holocaust. I believed it. That waste of riches and disgrace of manners I could never have imagined. It was a revelation of the possibility of human grandeur so terrific that my laborious, primitive disciplines cracked before it: the waters of life began to press, to seep through and wash out the crude, handpacked mortar; in an instant the last frantically thrown bags of sand and stones were swept away. I buckled and crumbled, and the seas of life flooded raging over the parching, deserted lots of my old self. And there I sat, stiff, quiet, drowning in my virgin tears.

That September the promised "adventure" of high school began. I was not deceived into eagerness by the exhortations of my friends and their teachers. While those mundane children exchanged their money for outfits for the crass mind —the clerical tools of scholarship like paper, bookcovers, briefcases, notebooks, pencils, pens, erasers, ink—and outfits for the unfledged body—combination locks, sneakers, T-shirts, shorts, socks, soap, I grudgingly gave as little as I could for the shoddiest stuff: all the rest I gladly spent on the movies, for the good of my soul. I walked to school; I went without lunch, without pie, without sodas. Yet, though I skimped and I scamped and I scavenged, I couldn't scrabble together enough to see more than three shows a week. How I bemoaned my folly and extravagance in not having saved three years' worth of Saturday quarters: forty dollars in tickets converted into unwanted crummy candy and crammed down my choking, ascetic throat! I was so despondent over the thought of my lamentable misled former life that it never occurred to me that even if I had used the money then as I now knew I should have, I would not be better off. Instead, I accused myself: You brainless, you! Why didn't you go? Because you didn't want to go and you ate to keep from being tempted to go! But why didn't you want to go? I talked to myself in this confusing circle for hours as I went from class to class, grinding my teeth absurdly in frustration. Time! I cried, Time is passing every minute! Each day without a movie was another void in my life, now that going to movies was not idle distraction but commitment to wonders of experience beyond my ken, vistas of superior knowledge that opened, perhaps, on a superior mode of life. I was appalled by the thought of looking back some year to a life full of empty holes in its weeks. I desired only to give myself over to the movies, to be so wholly possessed by them that I could feel their excess oozing from the pores in my stretched hide. I knew that to be free to enter the rare, special darkness of the theatre, I must cleanse myself of frivolous concerns; so I practiced preparing myself for the proper state by withdrawing attention from the six irrelevant waking hours spent in school and the three vacant afternoons a week I suffered from due to poverty, not to mention the energy frittered away on homework, dressing, undressing, washing, eating, basketball, sleep. Finally, since there was only one way to have money for those afternoons, I began to think of a part-time job. Part time! If I got a job, where then would be my time? The logic of my situation, when I sat down to consider elementary dilemmas in the dark corner of our simple, homely living room, made me pant and groan. However, it had to be faced. So I sold myself, quickly and shamelessly, to Mr. E. Golden, of the *Golden Pharmacy* under the El, across the street from the *RKO Royal,* around the corner from the *Loew's Imperial.*

The moment I saw this man I hated him. He was bald, obese, pasty yellow, stubble-faced. He had thick bifocal lenses that caught the light in two places. His shapeless tie was askew on a dirty white-on-white shirt with a pattern of fleurs-de-lis; his cuffs were pulled up on his hairy arms to his elephant-wrinkled elbows. His chronic expression was a sickeningly knowledgeable smile, and he looked out at the world over his eyeglasses. His hands were dirty

too, lying on the scratched glass counter and folding each other constantly or dealing out an infinitude of sundries, and taking in money, money, money. He never raised his voice, not in conversation, not in argument; but spoke questioningly at you like a rabbi. Your answers never fooled him, it seemed. I hated him as I sidled into the *Golden Pharmacy* and saw him standing by the cash register, pressing his pearl-buttoned, grey-smeared belly against the counter, hated him as I asked for the job delivering prescriptions and making myself "general handy" about the store, packing, unpacking, packaging, rummaging, sorting, sweeping —all for a quarter an hour, plus tips if any. I got the job right then— "But will you work good, sonny?" —and didn't learn till the end of the week why it was open: not a kid in the neighborhood would work for Golden the miser, the slavedriver, the taskmaster. I think the sort of nicknames he was given in the scrounging world of rabble boys, such as gold-grabber, kid-killer, miserymaniac, poison-pounder, soulsucker, show that he was held in awe as though he radiated occult might or perhaps an uncanny misery, even if contrary to the local superstition his piggish eyes were both the same colour:

grey, watery oil sloshing behind his steel-rimmed spectacles. Those popular names didn't matter to me, for I was going my own way, impervious to rumour and aura and history. Besides, the *Golden Pharmacy* was located on a rich, exciting corner, a crossroads of that section of the Bronx; everything in the world, almost, passed by or took place before its open door or was reflected in its Ex Lax and Feenamint-tattooed windows. Surely it was worth any boy's time just to be there, legitimately, to see and to learn while sweeping the sidewalk with careless industry, to snatch moments for meditation while wrapping sanitary napkins in anonymous blue paper for quick sale, and lettering them K-large, K-regular, K-small, and M-small, M-regular, M-large?

I went briskly to work for him. Again, in my proud, contrary way I was crazy to succeed where it could never even have occurred to the others. My ferocious addiction, far from the saturation point that marks the last stage in the descent to enlightenment of the lucky (or damned) person, made me that rarity, an enthusiastic slave. I hoped that by the end of the first week, I might win the approval from Mr. Golden necessary to the maintenance of my life. Though he was of course only a means to my end, as any master is for his slave, I hoped to betray him into a humane generosity so that he would deal with me gently, benevolently. And I used the most obvious means to propitiate this stolid man: my goodness. But he only grunted like a sleeping crocodile and never commented on my performance. No matter how many cartons I wrestled from the pavement outside, heaved between the showcases, around the chaos of boxes, bottles and brooms back of his prescription counter, down the narrow dangerous cellar steps, and dismantled, unwrapped, sorted, washing their contents and drying and arranging them on the grimy storage shelves in his tomb-lit basement; no matter how quick I was, how neat and tireless; no matter how fast I galloped delivering pills, syrupy nostrums and custom-made medicines and beauty formulas, returning with my cheeks glowing in a fever of self-congratulation (and a cold sweat drying on my spine), he only grunted, neither yes nor no. He would glance expressionlessly at me over his glinting bifocals as he went on heiratically wrapping a package precise and tight in the way he alone knew: folding the blue paper, creasing it straight and sharp with a stroke of the long, black-nailed, wicked index-finger, pulling out the green string that unrolled endlessly from the spool beneath the counter and winding it once-twice to the right, once-twice to the left, taking an extra length and twisting it around one pinky, around the other, pulling it taut, giving it a preliminary pflick, once! pflick, twice! and—snap! breaking it on the third, the real pull and then unconsciously tying the ends with some rapid passes and twirls that came out as inviolable knots. Well, that was the way he was—inscrutable. I could not guess whether he was amazed, suspicious, or downright resentful of the superb way I was working out; he only grunted and turned to his ceaseless argumentative deliberations, his quarrels and explanations with cosmetics salesmen, drug and sundries jobbers, and cranky grandmothers who detailed every symptom down to their slightest private twitchings, and complained about the behaviour of whatever limb, nerve, or organ he was helping them treat.

Sometimes I thought he waited maliciously for the foolish freckly grin I couldn't hold back which announced that some chore had been accomplished beyond his most liberal expectations, to say, "Nu, sonny, next! Take these pills to Mrs. Katz on Eastchester Avenue. Quick, quick! They're for her husband, he's got heart trouble, he's sick, he might die if you don't come soon. Here's change for ten dollars—" Bing! the cash register opens, there is the accurate, unhurryable counting-out, and Bang! the drawer is thrown shut—"and you don't need carfare, it's only ten blocks. And come back right away, I got one for the other side of the park." And when I'd climbed the fifth flight and stood gasping before that unidentified door which was scratched by penknives with hearts and initials and swastikas Xed-out but re-engraved, Mrs. Katz would invariably be one of those late middle-aged crones who called out, "Who's there?" quaveringly from a remote cubicle at the end of her echoing, dank apartment. Out of breath, embarrassed by my saving presence at the scene of some typically incurable human emergency, I'd yell, garbling the words to save Mrs. Katz from the curiosity of her pitying neighbours, "It's me, the druggist boy."

"Yeh? What do you want?"

I would not answer again because I despised Mrs. Katz. I could hear her come shuffling in her soggy, filthy mules, nastily, rheumatically along the empty linoleum-floored hall. She would fumble at the peephole; then her invisible face would put its rancorous bleary pupil to it.

But I would be too close for her to see more than another staring eye. A little scared, maybe, Mrs. Katz would say again, "Who is it?"

Now I stepped back and declared in a voice ringing with offended simplicity, "It's only me, from the *Golden Pharmacy!"*

And then, Mrs. Katz changed, instantaneously, from a defenceless creature into an abused, sorrowful, wailing, almost possessed mourner at a funeral which had not yet occurred, and might not for years. "Oi! Weh! The medicine. Oi! Weh! God help me, how long you take. Oi Weh! You're heartless! We're sick, dying, you bastards! Oi! Weh!" And then she would fumble at the chain of the police lock in the gloom of her unlighted foyer, and then the doorlatch's lock; she would give a pull and discover she'd double-locked the police lock, so then that would be turned two or three times, opening and shutting the baffling, cranky bolt. At last, the door would give, only a crack, and this Mrs. Katz would snatch her faded, greasy, flower-quilted house-coat to her in miserable modesty, having revealed the top of her grey breast, that drawn-down dug—why wasn't she ever dressed!—and strike the grey hank of iron hair back from her temple, and look bleakly out at this sleetsparkling kid in his shiny, new, belted and fur-collared leather mackintosh, who stood panting with fatigue and impatience to be gone again (but first to impersonate the cherub of mercy and salvation himself so that he would be tipped, a quarter maybe, a half-dollar even—who knew?). And how, having forgotten the tedious process of her approach and opening to my summons, she would say, "Yeh? What is it?"

Unctuously then, I would resume our ritual, "I'm Mr. Golden's boy. With the prescription for Mr. Katz. It's the rush order . . . I think?"

"You're Golden's boy?"

"Yeah, the new boy. I deliver now."

"Yeh? Okay. So how much is it?"

"Five eighty-three. It says so here on the box."

"Oi, weh! Five eighty-three! Robber! Murder! He should drop dead from cancer. It should eat your heart, Golden, you thief!"

That was the payoff; that, I knew, was the end of my four-bit dream, my vain hope to cash in on Mrs. Katz's gratitude, her surge of old-world, courteously embroidered thanksgiving for my miraculous messengership. Didn't she realize how far I had come?

"You got change from ten, sonny?"

I would hand the prescription to her, avoiding the touch of those raspy, dry fingers, and reach into my mackintosh's secret zipper pocket for the change. Still painfully shuffling, Mrs. Katz would disappear back into her vague, staled, chicken-soupy apartment, returning with a crumpled ten; she would take my four-seventeen and put it all into a worn, leather snap purse, and then wait in doubt while I stood there unmoving, shaming her. An awkward silence, until with a sly smile she said, "Oi, weh! Here's for you, boy. A tip." Into my open, humiliated palm, she would drop, first the two pennies, and next, as with all my power I wished the dime away from her— at least that dime—she fished around in the purse (oh I knew she'd put the change away first so that she'd be forcing herself, so full of virtue, to give me her own money instead of permitting me to keep a decent portion of my change in my own hands), and inevitably not the dime but the nickel would be the award. And then I squeezed out a faint "Thank you very much indeed, Mrs. Katz," over my shoulder as I receded down the stairwell, hotly cursing her under my breath, her purse, her pains, her medicine, and cursing poor Mr. Katz too, whom surely she

and Golden were conspiring to kill.

It was falling into November. The sooty, chilling November rain of sleet drifted through the light of the streetlamps as I stumbled back the more than ten blocks to the *Golden Pharmacy* through the emptied five o'clock streets and over the black burnt-over lots. My shoes were stiff with damp, shrivelling cold that broke the seams; my heels would have rubbed through my socks by now, blisters would have formed, broken, and been scarified into raw, red half-dollars of morbidity.

But I stuck to it, obstinate. Lacking any evidence whatsoever, I'd found it the more necessary to convince myself I'd proved indispensable, a wonder worker, and that Mr. Golden not only needed me but by now wanted me. It seemed to me that his business had picked up because my delivery was so accurate and prompt, that people were telling their friends to come to the *Golden Pharmacy,* and even bought more prescriptions than the doctors ordered, just so I could arrive grinning at their doors. How could it be otherwise? It didn't occur to me that winter made them sick. Also, Golden could never have expected to get so much out of a boy for a mere quarter of a dollar an hour: surely he would give me a raise soon? Naturally I should not ask him. How would I bring it up? He might easily wax wrathful and fire me like a shot; that was the risk I couldn't afford. Every week, just before the dramatic moment at ten o'clock on Saturday night when my six dollars and twenty-five cents was due, I fretted myself into a state of hope mingled with indignation: hope that he would count out the extra dollar twenty-five bounty I deserved, and indignation in my fantasy that I would have the courage to blurt out my demand for a nickel an hour more in wages and be gallingly rejected. Upon which, spontaneously of course, I should tell him what a rat he was, maybe kick a hole in the sliding glass door of the vitamin cabinet and—be arrested, sent to jail?—and quit. I quit! Do you hear me? Do you understand me, Mr. Golden? I quit! Naturally, it never happened that way.

And Sundays I brooded all morning, standing beneath my mother's wet, dripping wash in the bathroom, and glowering at the mirror where I saw myself, the original yellow yellow. But in the afternoon I soothed my anguish in the dark, people-packed Sunday Matinee (expensive!) movies to which I went—across the Bronx by taxi—in the immense Counter-Reformation cathedral known as the _Loew's Paradise_. There, the mezzanine lobby was a way station full of marble alcoves and chambers furnished with gilded baroque furniture for those who loitered between the blurred throngs and grey traffic of the Grand Concourse and the ecstasy within; there, the bathrooms were Venetian delights, little palaces wherein one was privileged to go; there, inside, far above, the constellations moved forever past a pale Cyprian horn of moon, and simulated clouds drifted always under that deeply vaulted though fake sky, and far down below, the fat seats slid back and forth instead of tilting up, the backs reclining in rhythm with the seats. There in that house of worship I melted in filial gratitude toward the impossible Mr. Golden, and soon forgave him, and easily forgot him.

After two months of this strenuous equilibrium between spiritual debauch and the labour of wresting a meagre living from Golden's killing schedules, lung and limb became adapted and I knew I could take it.

December lowered on New York, horrid with clinkered slush and sewers stuffed with polluted snow. In the gutters at corners, scrapings and chippings of sidewalk ice floated in two or three inches of black, sludgy, freezing water. The northeast wind blew virulent in your face and whistled agues down your back at turnings and through the open spaces, and you went in and out of this marrow-cracking weather, from drowning cold to dry overheated hallways and apartments where people had only to hawk once and you came down with shakes, dragged in an hour from prime strength into the suicidal gloominess of the flu. That is how New York's exasperating winter has always gone; but that year I was impervious to mere weather and impermeable to the invisible creatures of the blast. As in a plague, people fell away with one pharynge-bronchial thing and another; yet I kept moving, godling-like, twin to the cardboard Hermes displayed in our store window who bounced eternally oscillant back and forth, driven by the miniature electric motor which was hitched to a set of gimcrack rubber-band pulleys. The pandemic grew so intense that I was seldom present in the *Golden Pharmacy* except to touch home and start off again. In those December days I conceived of myself as a pathetic, demerit-burdened minor angel condemned for some short time to the misery of this biting, deathray-ridden solar system of Sol's, working off my penalty by dangerous flights through frozen space which were necessary to the grander scheme of the central bureau. I was continually posting hither and yon over the East Bronx, delivering Golden goods; there was just no time left to stand and serve at the counter. I was satisfied with my lot, and confident I satisfied. Yet, one afternoon when Golden held up a monitory palm and commanded me to stop right where I was and take off my coat, I had a shiver of alarm. I thought, perhaps Mr. Golden had become used to the dustlessness and new order I'd brought to his neglected showcases, too used to freedom from the trash he'd formerly stumbled through behind his counters. Hadn't he seemed morose now that I was not around, a sweating and heaving, shrimpy Hercules? Had he seen that I thought myself a free agent, a sort of self-administered contact man between his prescription table and the ailing who clamoured for his costly salvations? Had he caught me looking too saucily at him as if I thought *he* was the dependent, unable to survive without *me?* Had I been so noticeable swaggering and strutting before him, like a child of the wastes and wild places, the illiterate random Bedouin daring him to challenge his roving habits?

94

Or maybe, so I half-hoped, he missed me a little, and wanted a dose of my unwashed sunny spirits every so often to relieve the monotony of his days at the store, that oasis and midden where he squatted loaded down by the trivial and numberless civilized luxuries he dealt in, and bored by the endless vulgar colour and variety which streamed through it every day, and which weighed on his soul in that depot of fateless things? Whatever the reason, when I came rushing in, trying to avoid his eye and in my self-begotten autonomy get efficiently out again, he said, "Sonny, hey! What took so long?"

"Well, Mr. Golden. I had that order for near Parkchester, and the other one, the package the old lady phoned for, down on West-chester, so I took both at once and—"

"Okay, okay. Wait a minute, will you, please?"

"But—"

"What's your rush? Wait!"

"But I have this medicine to take to near Gunhill, and this one for Burke Avenue—" and I reached audaciously into the cash-register for change.

"No, I say! It's Friday. I want you should stay here. It's getting rush hour; everybody's coming home. You stay and sweep up. Take these cartons"—they were three great heavy ones I'd left plunk in the middle of the store for two days now, effectively having wished them, in my mind at least, into invisibility—"and break them down. Then you go and work that counter for the girls when they come in tonight—you know, all that junk they want for the week-end."

"But Mr. Golden," I said righteously—really, I was a fanatic about *running* the damn prescrip-tions, although I'd lost my illusions about the necessity for speeding them through, having seen that sick people either go to the hospital, die, or have someone come to wait for the stuff to be made up— "I *must* take these orders. You said before Mrs. Schluge called twice, and Mr. Kyron is *really* bad this time."

"Never mind what I said. You stop thinking and running where you please, and get those cartons down from there."

"Well, all right. But how will those orders—?"

"Gott! I say never mind them orders!" And then, as an after-thought, he remarked casually, perhaps to mollify the spurious expression of conscience-stricken concern I wore, or perhaps to explode it, "They will be taken care of, Joey. Don't you worry." He raised his eyebrows ambiguously at me over his shoulder, "Hey! Come up here now."

I couldn't believe my ears. Was I being fired tonight? On a Friday? But why? My racing heart trembled like a melting jelly. I hadn't meant to seem that rambunctious and uppity. I really hadn't! In truth, I was still assiduous, and as faithful. Just because I left a few cartons . . . But he himself knew how I'd been dashing every minute all week. What? What? But then, I was being promoted, kind of, wasn't I? I was to put on the grey cotton jacket, wash my hands, and select sundries with such comprehension and discrimination for the girls who came for cosmetics before their weekend dating, and help the guys who asked shyly for their tins of Ramses or Trojans (just in case), and the people old and young who wanted to buy Christmas presents of toilet water, special soaps like Bouquet de New York, powder sets, fountain pens, after-shave lotion, and whatnot. And, I would be working the cash-register constantly, touching and folding twenties as I liked, making change and serving so pleasantly the myriad folk who came to me needy in unending lines. And yet, I could not help suspecting that I had somehow displeased Mr. Golden, had failed him, or failed to make him believe in me. It also occurred to me right then that if he had been decent he would have consulted me about how much work there really was, asked my opinion as to whether I could not speed up, or work both the in and the outsides of the job by re-arranging deliveries on a systematic schedule instead of running when each order was prepared; and that if he had done the right thing and begged for my considered judgment, I could have told him, oh so judiciously and with suggestive cunning, that he could avoid shelling out two wages by having me step up my output and pay me half an additional worker's money (which would not be *quite* the same thing as a raise from him, but for me a raise nevertheless). So as I waited numb with surprise, chewing and swallowing these chagrined thoughts and rueing my simplicity in having taken my control of Golden for granted, he shouted again, "Hey, you! You heard me? I said come here!" Now there were indeed feet on the cellar stairs. Unhurrying steps they were indeed. Then this other kid came out.

God! Where could he have come from! *Keerist!* In our neighbourhood teeming with kids, how had he remained unknown to me and my friends? What a hideola! A ratty belt several sizes too large, the gnawed end of which dangled in front of his half-zipped fly, barely held up his brown corduroy knickers, and their frayed cuffs hung down his skinny shanks to his ankles where absurdly big feet were cased in heavy, heelworn brown rubbers. He wore a flannel shirt of rusted green plaid; over that a brown-buttoned, unbuttoned, old man's black wool cardigan, the unravelling cuffs protruding from the sleeves of a too large, too heavy, hairy, three-quarter coat of checkered black and orange boxes. His clammy blue hands looked like worms in specimen bottles; the nails had been· bitten down and were replaced by scarred palps of nibbled flesh. And his head! That face! The skull rose to a point behind; mousy, pig-bristle hair; the mouth was open, slack, slavering, full of tiny round blueblack teeth which were lead-braced and hooked top and bottom by rubber bands; eyeglasses round as the bottom of a six-cent Woolworth water glass behind which bulbous grey eyes swam, out of phase and out of focus; the frame of those glasses was held· together where it had been broken, by friction tape on the bridge of his devious, green-clotted nose—and that whole grease and pimpled face had a gross allotment of knobbly warts overrunning it, from the back of his neck on up through his scalp. My stomach twisted over with rage, and outrage, at this apparition. That *that* was what Golden was willing to settle for! That sullen, nasty kid fit to do my splendid work? What a travesty of the fine image I had of myself: the worker worthy of his work, the work worthy of the worker, evoking from him a beautiful intensity which he embodied in the swift clean responses of a dancer intuitively moving to music he has not heard before. Even were I not so trammelled in the gorgeous garment I threw about myself everywhere, I should not have been capable of understanding who that creature was or why he was there, and what criticism it cast upon my notions of what was important in the world, of what meant what and to whom. As I changed into my clerking dustcoat I watched him chew and blow and pop a wad of skyblue bubble-gum and listen absently to Golden's directions and take the money for change from him with a disrespectful, nay insulting lack of interest, and stuff the precisely-wrapped medicine bottle—rolled with such finesse in its striped green paper by Golden, the top of the wrapping twisted once into a locked spill so that no string or scotchtape was necessary to seal it—into his pocket carelessly, as if it didn't matter that the bottle might slip out and spill its precious contents en route. Mr. Golden for his part seemed not even to notice the rudeness. What were my ideal efforts worth? It was incredible! Callous, unrushed, he slouched out of the store; passing the window outside, he peeled a strip off Mr. Golden's Notary Public seal, and left that officially scarlet badge, that important legal sunburst, a mere slice of old tomato with a bite taken out. This was but the absurd beginnings of my trouble. Right off, I caught its sensational tone: it gave me a whiff of the exasperation and horror I was in for as I dwindled into a mere butt for derisory amusement.

The next night, for instance, was Saturday. When business slowed after the dinner hour, I went down to the cellar to flatten cartons for the garbage collectors who came after midnight, and gather together the trash of wrappings and packings I'd left from my week's hectic dispensing. He was reclining down there in the murk on a heap of corrugated litter under the steps. Perhaps he thought I had cut him, as if I were yesterday's favourite vexed at feeling myself slipping into obscurity? Well, one could not let an interloper think that. I would not show my bitter temper; frank and securely genial, that would be my style. I should, since that *thing* was evidently good enough in Mr. Golden's eyes to be enlisted—and having hired me, he ought to know what a man was worth—I should not behave in any way that might impair the felicity and efficiency of our organization. After all, wasn't it probable that he was not conscious of his unfortunate appearance to others? Though he was unhappy, might he not be good nevertheless? He could even turn out rather helpful; with proper handling he might work into the job. I wasn't one to spoil things. So I planned my approach carefully: I set to work clearing the floor, fitting things neatly into each other, gathering up loose ends, making symmetrical piles of cardboard and tying them tightly, just so, using no more twine than necessary, and shifting them into stable heaps in one place. I hummed a little workmanlike tune and whistled while I worked, off-key, between my teeth, absent-mindedly, to create a busy warehouse scene. After I had swept out and cleared the stage, I sat down at the table and started ranging raw bottles together according to their colour, quality, size: brown heavy ones for big pills;

quarter-pint and half-pint clear white bottles for cough medicine; clear pint bottles for the Special Secret Formula Golden Lotion; small brown round bottles for expensive pills, vitamins and such; and flat brown round minijars for the Mystic Golden Unguent and the Golden Sun Pomatum. Next, I had to select proper-sized stoppers and black plastic screw caps for each lot. Before doing that, I turned around for a break, ingenuously, and said, "You're the new boy here, eh?" No answer. I said, louder, "You're going to be working with us from now on, eh?"

A barely audible sign came from under the stairs: "Huh?"

"I said—"

My polite repetition was interrupted by a bored snarl, "Yeah, yeah, I heard you. So what?"

"Well, I thought, since we have to be working here together, we might as well get acquainted, you know, and see what has to be done. Sort of have a conference and, uh, divide up the chores properly, you know?"

A shaft of giggling. I persevered. "Say, uh, my name's Joey, fellah. What's yours?"

Giggling again, he said, "Sam-u-el."

"Okay, Sammy, how's about it?" Silence. "We'll divvy up the cleaning down here until you catch on and learn how to do it quick for yourself. After all, I have to spend a lot of time on the counter up front, you know. And then, well, we can share up the orders even-steven— once you, once me—so's the tips work out pretty much the same. Uh, confidentially, they mostly stink, anyway."

"No," he said, louder still and shrilly, "No. Sam-u-el! No Sammy, hear me?" He was scrambling out from under the stairs.

"Sam-u-el? What kinda name's that?"

"Sam-u-el!" he said, glaring at me with those watering eyeballs.

"Okay. Take it easy! Suits you, suits me. Sam-u-el. Sam-u-el, okay?" I laughed, patronizingly. "Sam! U! El!" If that was the only name he'd answer to—so? A jerk, I thought; a moron.

"Now, how about giving me a hand here with these bottles? I'll call out the size, and you get the bottle caps down from the boxes there."

He looked at me once, curiously, and started back for the stairs.

"Hey!" I called, "Sam-u-el! How's about a hand here—it's part of the job."

"Screw you," he said, crawling back into his retreat. A fat lot of help he'd be! Later, taking the washed and sparkling glassware up to Golden, I looked down between the steps and thought I could see him lying there. One hand was in his mouth, he was gnawing the thumb; the other seemed to be squirming around inside his pants.

Things in the cellar were not ever to be improved. With or without my direction, Sam-u-el had no desire to co-operate; in fact, I came to believe he didn't intend working at all. I couldn't imagine why Golden kept him on, for on the job he certainly was not, responding only after long delay to the Golden summons—one cry, "Hey, sonny!" and one stomp-stomp overhead— and dragging along as though through quicksand out into the whining, murky-winded winter street. Soon I saw why he was so slow to answer. He had built himself a den down there under the stairs, a kind of comfortable troglodyte's home, floored with corrugated cardboard carton-liners and pillowed, sided, and shelved with detective and screen magazines. In my compulsive cleaning up, I would have to collect the photos of movie people, the cheesecake, glamorous, workaday and recreational pictures (swim? dance? golf? tennis? drive the convertible? lunch-cocktails - dinner - soirée - banquet - function?) which he tore out, stuck up and gazed at for a minute, and then defiled, crushed, and tossed over his threshold like so many cracked and cleaned bones. I couldn't see the reason of his passion for those stupid, wooden magazines full of stars and stareens, starlings and starlets all so fit and grinning at you, when only a movie could bring them to life so variously and so well-disguised that they became multitudinously incarnate real people, instead of remaining the mere abstractions of cheap publicity, sterile for evermore. Nor could I appreciate why he looked at those tawdry "official" police photographs: the trampled grass at the edge of the stagnant pond where the rusty hatchet was found, and then, a few yards on, the battered and broken body of Beatrice Zyzwlinskzi, glared by the flashbulb, and the same mono-chrome, unsolved scene shown in daylight, or the old leather-and-iron-bound steamer trunk opened by a curious child in some rooming-house attic, stuffed with the naked honeymooners whose matted, blood-clotted heads are just visible twisted awry on their gory white torsos, while detectives in blueblack striped serge stand vacuously about, confused and bored, paunch-vested and badged and fat-faced under their fedoras, wondering, what now was what? I thought, at least a kid Sam-u-el's age could be reading men's adventure magazines, or, since it was such as he, Katzen-jammer comic-books; not those dull, repetitive crime things littered with snapshots of the guns and bullets and butcher-knives and grenades and home-made bombs and whips which had been cached in this place or seized in that place, or the manacles from which the girl had been suspended left dangling in the other place. Because I was hating so hard, I did not understand that Sam-u-el's idea of spiritual reality was not so different from mine; I was too full of repulsion from that dirty, scoffing, drooling, and yes, he smoked also, moronic little warthog. I did not recognize that the only difference between us was that he worshipped alone, a cenobite and rebel, while I sat for three hours and a half at a stretch with the adoring, demotic mob in my regular, thrice-weekly retreats to those mixed monasteries, the movies. Most important, I couldn't see that though his icons were static, they were closer than mine, in a way, to the actual, because his were private and served himself alone there in his rooted-out cave, while mine, though enormous and moving in their expensive temples, were ultimately utterly false. But, also,

I discovered that he was deeper into esoteric wisdom than I, that he was an ecstatic with original, peculiarly depraved and bestial rituals.

One sleeting afternoon in January when it was good to be among warm, dry, dusty boxes, I heard him snuffling with what I took to be amusement. I walked over to see what was going on. At the door to his wallow, some of the packs of Camels he'd stolen from my counter upstairs had been stood together to form a small box that contained about forty or fifty loose cigarettes, while a dozen or so matchbooks were arranged around it to make a five-pointed star. He was leaning back between two burning faintly incensed votive candles in violet and orange glasses. He looked up. "Hey, Joey, didja ever hear this song?" Without waiting for a reply he crooned out:

"I took my girl to the ballgame
And sat her right up front,
Along came a baseball
And hit her in the—

Country boy, *country* boy,
Sitting on a rock,
Along flies a bumblebee
And stings him in the—

Cocktail, gingerale,
Five cents a glass,
And if you don't like it,
Put it up your—

Ask me no questions,
I'll tell you no lies . . ."

A stupid kid's song; it meant nothing to me. "So what?" I said. "You know something? You're a jerk, Sam-u-el." I was going away when he called out mysteriously, "Hey, Joey, wanna see something?" When I said, dubiously, yes, wishing he would stop annoying me, he motioned me to creep in with him. I did.

Spreading a pack of playing cards out face down, he told me to turn one up. I thought it was silly gambling, and immediately regretted I'd gone in only to be enlisted in some boring game like Go Fish or Casino. He lit a fresh cigarette for himself from the purple candle. I turned a card over. There was a picture on the other side. I looked at it, and was shocked. It was a photo of a fat, naked, peroxide blonde of about forty-five, eh old! blowsy-bellied and balloon-dugged. She was hunkered over a pot, and she was grinning inanely at me. I could see, by staring hard at the black patch between her legs, that she was peeing. Sam-u-el snortled again. "Funny, hah? Take another." I turned a card again. This one had a picture of a skinny, naked man who still wore his shoes; his socks were stretched up on his shins with garters. He had plastered, shiny hair, parted down the middle and worn like they did in the old movies; he had a handlebar moustache and his face, though he looked me straight in the eye, was void of expression. The same blonde woman was bent over before him, still grinning; her baggy tits hung low; apparently her backside was pressed up against his stomach, though I couldn't see what for. "What the hell—?" I said. "Take one; go wan." I turned up yet another, fascinated but repelled. It showed the same dead-panned man (I could tell by the socks and shoes and moustache) and two ladies now (I thought of them as "ladies" on account of their age). The man was lying on his back on an old brass bed; there was a rubber plant in the corner of the room, an old-fashioned room such as you saw in Chaplin movies. Both the ladies were on the bed with him, on their hands and knees like dogs. It was hard to imagine what they were up to. Sam-u-el must have seen the horrified astonishment on my face. He tore the card out of my numb fingers. "Interesting, hah? Lemmee see. Ooh, that's good." He stuck his cigarette in the side of his mouth, threw his head back on the bolster of *Crime Confessions,* held the card above his face with one hand where he could make it out in the flickering orange-violet light, ripped open his fly with the other and began jerking at himself, making those little snuffling noises. I scrambled out, taking extra care not to upset his altar of cigarettes, so leery and fearful had I grown of disturbing his peculiar ways. I was dizzy, and I felt like throwing up. So that was what he did in there. That little . . . And that's what he used those full-page pictures of movie stars for, and had the gall then to throw them out for *me* to sweep, along with his cigarette stubs and chewing-gum wrappers and Babe Ruth wrappers and what all else. So much I loathed him, that I decided, against the clear advice of my intuition, to get him out right away. The next afternoon I went to Mr. Golden and said, "Mr. Golden, I have to tell you this—" my breath came irregularly no matter how I tried to calm it "—about him."

"Who?"

"That kid down there. He's not such a good worker—you know?" The questioning note tacked itself on to my declaration of its own accord.

"Yeh?" I didn't like the way he smiled, so knowledgeably, at me and raised his eyebrows as if he knew all about whatever I was going to say (though I myself did not), and was amused by it no end.

"And he doesn't help me clean up, or sort out, or sweep, or anything. He even *makes* dirt!"

"So?"

"Well, you know, I'm doing it all anyway, and so . . ."

"So?" The man was impossible! Why did I have to state it, when he should have taken over the line of investigation I had suggested and come to his own conclusions?

"Well—what *good* is he? You're wasting your money on him."

That stroke, appealing to the money angle, would surely do it, I thought. I was wrong.

"*Your* business?"

"Well no. But it's a shame, I think. Maybe you should try to get somebody else? I mean, if you *really* think you need two men?"

"Yeh?"

What more could I say to him? He didn't seem to pay the least attention to the importance, or the gravity, especially from the business-like point of view, of my charge. I was baffled. Would I ever understand him? "Look, sonny," he said, after watching me change legs a couple of times, and with that sphinxy smile on his face that said nothing yet hinted all, "you go mind your counter there for a while. Yeh?" I went, grinding my molars, red-necked with shame and defeat. He returned to the sanctum of his prescription bench. How terrible, now that I was in an almost intolerable passion of disgust, to be forced to recognize that there was no other way but to suffer it, though the sight and sound of that Sam-u-el, his mere presence in the cellar, made my mouth tingle and water with metallic nausea.

For the next half hour I could hear Golden busily making up prescriptions and things, weighing, pouring, scraping, pestling away in his mortar, screwing on caps, moving gallon bottles of basics around, typing up labels, and wrapping. Frequently, I'd glimpse the light bouncing off his glasses as he looked through the plate glass screen at me. Finally, he called down, "Sam-u-el?" The usual long silence. I smiled to myself, vindicated. "Sam-u-el!" *Stomp-stomp*. Then at last, those clumsy feet climbing the wooden stairs. "Take this order to number 39." That must be in the building upstairs, I thought. Another long pause. "Well? Get going." Silence. Then Sam-u-el said, "No." Even I, predictor that I was, was surprised by that flat refusal. "What do you mean, No?" Golden said. "No—No is No!" I was elated. That would finish him. I stood perfectly still, waiting to rejoice

when the wall fell on him. There was no crash. Golden sighed, then looked in my direction. "Joey! You heard me?" "Yes sir yes sir yes sir," I said. I took off my clerking coat and went for the package. Sam-u-el stood there yet, looking mean and stubbornly unrepentant. Golden paid him no attention. I went out, puzzled.

Though the store was on the ground floor and occupied a good space on its busy corner, I'd not been into this apartment house and had never noticed just how immense *The Alexandria* was. I had to go two blocks, clear around two corners, to find the entrance which, guarded by a pair of unsexed concrete lions whose fangs had been knocked off, was a Moorish archway of brown and yellow bricks encrusted with tiny sculptures that also gave it vaguely Byzantine echoes. Its name, *The Alexandria,* broken up here and there and embellished with chalk by children, was spelled in mosaic on the pavement of the inner courtyard just beyond the arch; there were also potsy squares around it, a flock of grotesque, coloured, hieratic figures, childishly formal, and lovers' broken hearts and names scrawled vulgarly on the pink concrete of the walk. It was an old building, one of the grandiose monuments from the early times of the neighbourhood, mannered and regal in ground plan. The lobby had carved, blackish-brown oak furniture, gigantic thrones and chests and sideboards with empty brass candelabra and other useless, elaborate objects like trays and bowls; the elevators were capacious, disguised as elegant antechambers, and must once upon a time have been operated by uniformed boys, as the dead wheels with handles indicated, but had long since been converted to modern self-service machines. There were actually four sections to this great apartment house, arranged in a quadrangle around seven rotting Lombardy poplars, as tall as the cornices on the roof, which stood in a neglected leafless garden that was not much more grassless and dead in January than it would be in June. Each wing of the house had its own elevator, but the hallways met at the corners through low firedoors with arched lintels, doors chained open regardless of the law. Four wings meant there were four apartments numbered 39, probably all alike in layout; they were on the sixth floor: 39-North, 39-East, 39-South, 39-West. Golden hadn't told me which to seek. I didn't care for returning to the store, so I wandered along those faded, varnished stucco halls, pleased for the moment with the cavernous sorrows of these crypts cut into by deep-set steel doors, behind which reposed the bodies of richer, better people. I stopped at 39-South. What difference did it make? If I was wrong, I would move onward to the west. When I pushed the doorbell button, I was pleasantly surprised; instead of the raucous blatting of the usual painted-over buzzer, a noise that, always made my heart sink because I feared it would bring me Mrs. Katz, I heard a distant set of chimes, four notes down, four up again. They were slow chimes, golden and warmly vibrant, and carolled to each other. I felt instantly calmer; why should I be upset over carrying this order for Sam-u-el? I think the chimes sounded a broken chord that soothed.

There was no answer. But Golden must have known someone would be home—he wouldn't have had a delivery made for nothing. So, I gladly set them off again: Ding! Deng! Dang! Dong! they rang, and after pausing, back up once more, Dong! Dang! Deng! Ding! they sung. Then a woman's voice called from a long way off, tunefully and slow, "Come in." I tried the door; it was unlocked. I walked in. To my eyes, accustomed to the penurious squalour of my parsimonious Katzes and Schluges and Kroynses, this was an Alhambra. Not scuffed linoleum, but carpeting from wall to wall. Three foot high porcelain lamps, glazed sylvan scenes depicted on them, stood on round leather-topped mahogany end-tables. There were deep armchairs and couches covered with nubby silk brocades of watery-hued oriental magentas and turquoises, citron, saffron and emerald. There were credenzas of mahogany in which cut-crystal wine-glasses stood poised. There were real, painted pictures — flowers, ships, landscapes of the winter and summer with mists and peasant cottages and cattle—hung in gilded, carved frames which had little lights attached at the top to light them. And here and there painted plates, and silver and gold dishes with figures hammered in them hung on the walls, and mirrors everywhere, ornate, glass-framed, large and small — everywhere mirrors. Before the windows at the far wall was a black lacquer stand, and on it a great cinnabar vase, intricately chiselled with pagodas and sages and flowers, which contained a whole armful of gladioli, as in a funeral parlour. Drawn back, the plum velvet draperies exposed white silk curtains on which the light moved soft after filtering through the tripe-width venetian blinds. Nor were the walls one colour; some were painted pink or brown, some were actually papered, and the wallpapers showed bucolic scenes or unique arrangements of rare flowers in bunches two feet high. And there was, to complete that suave enchantment of my senses, a waltzy music lulling and lilting from a Chinese - modern ebony cabinet. I stood, gaping at the inexpressible beauty of this living room into which one descended by four steps that were flanked by wrought - iron, gilded railings. I drank it in. "Hello?" I called, not too harshly, to preserve this peace.

"Come in, come in," she said from somewhere, whispering the words again, singing them it seemed. I tiptoed down the long carpeted foyer, following the perfumed echo of her voice. There were turns; I opened some closet doors by mistake, closets stuffed with linens and clothes, and I stepped into two bathrooms—two of them! big bathrooms tiled all the way to the ceiling, one with all its fixtures pink and one green, with a green sink, green tub, green toilet! Finally, I found the way and came to the door of a bedroom lit lemon pale by the January sun which hung low in the south over Manhattan, and was dropping beyond the Consolidated Edison gas tank that marked the low bottom of the Bronx.

"Come here," she said quietly. Her tone was not one of request, but expectant and sure of fulfillment. I crossed the room; the rug my unpolished, squaretoed brogans walked on was orange-brown, over-woven with green flowerets; the elegant furniture was rosewood, carved and glistening with oil; there was a froth of white and gauzy curtain cascading from the windows, a field of scarlet covered the bed. A door led to a small yellow bathroom, and another to an adjoining bedroom which was not so sumptuous as this one since it lacked the glorious thing to which my eyes were drawn: the enormous vanity table, mirror-backed and mirror-topped. All the light in the room it gathered into itself and condensed there, like shimmering silver, making the room insubstantial, unbounded by walls. It occurred to me that she slept alone in that enormous bed, and that the other room belonged to the Master of the house. Master and Mistress were the terms that came to me—straight from my complete handbook of filmic lore. And she (the mistress) sat on a pink stool before that vanity; she did not turn, but watched me in the mirror. I could not see her face, but I knew she must be very beautiful. She wore a heavy satin kimono, so white it

had a shade of steel-blue in its surface, like frost-bitten cheeks; it was gaudily, magnificently embroidered with a rampant dragon whose head reposed in flames over her left shoulder, whose short, gouging forelegs reached rudely under her left arm, whose burning, mica-plated, flexible torso stretched the length of her spine; whose punishing lower limbs grasped her hips (one extended talon seemed to be clutching her left hip, the other was fastened into her right hip), and whose armored tail coiled over and around in front and enveloped, I supposed, her thighs. Her hair was long and of a jet black colour I'd never seen—it glowed with violet highlights. It was spread out on her shoulders and she brushed it with languorous strokes, the movement of her arms causing the great reptile on her back to undulate in slow passion, as if he was a god coming gradually to life. I couldn't keep my eyes off it. At once I thought of her, and was ashamed at my reversion to comic strip puerility, as the fabulous Eurasian in "Terry and the Pirates" — none other than the Dragon Lady herself, that mysterious, fatal bandit and vamp of the South China Seas.

"What do you want?" she said. Did I detect an exotic accent? Had I come to the right place?

"Here's your order you sent for from the *Golden Pharmacy,* Madame?" Before I could help it, I began to kowtow, but stopped gracefully short of that and offered her my lumpy package with just the right indication of noble, squiring courtesy.

"Golden Pharmacy?" she echoed, bemused. "Did I order anything special today? I don't think so; but . . . However . . ."

"Ah, Madame, I must be mistaken," I said, meaning again to say, Ma'am, but the instinct of servility had possessed me—I didn't know why except that I felt such a personage ought to be addressed in that manner.

"No, it must be a surprise. Mr. Golden knows what I require. And Mr. Golden always has it here in time."

She was a regular customer then? I wondered why I had never been sent up in all these months. She turned around and took the package from me. Her eyebrows were heavy and black, the lashes long and black and gummy, the lids faintly aquamarine, like the evening sky above the horizon. Her eyes were large; glowing. Her face was powdered deathly white. A pale red suffused her cheeks. Her mouth was a wide, red, enamelled gash filled with large even teeth, except

for a place where a molar seemed to be missing on top at back; also I could see gold caps on the bottom row towards the back. The kimono was held together at the lowest part of the deep V between her breasts by a couchant gold· dragon which had red stones for eyes (rubies, I guessed). The silk tassels of the scarlet sash lay along her legs and drooped over her knees to the floor. Her white-ankled, blue-veined feet wore Chinese slippers of scarlet, beaded felt.

She unwrapped the parcel on her lap, smiling in a pleased way as she read the labels of that assortment of pomades, unguents, creams and lotions, marbled liquids and burning chemicals—all custom-blended, as I well knew. One at a time she placed them on the mirrored top of her vanity, stretching and swivelling half-around, her hand drawing the kimono closed again, too late, every time she turned back to pick another from her lap. I was not conscious that I stared at her; I was all petrified stare. When she was done, she crushed the wrapper and string into a ball and tossed it carelessly towards a pink-quilted basket in the corner of the room. Without thinking whether I ought to, I went to put it in.

"Thank you, very much," she said. She actually had a queer

accent, concealed but noticeable. "Now. I suppose you are Mr. Golden's new boy?"

"Yes, Madame."

"How long have you been working for him?"

"Five months, Madame."

"Five months? Why have I never seen you before? What is your name?" I hesitated. For such as she, I thought, it should not be Joey or Joe as my parents, my friends, my teachers called me, but the name I'd never used. I wondered if I could even pronounce it with conviction. It would be funny to hear it, but I took the chance: "Joseph is my name. But I'm called—"

"Ah! Joseph! A beautiful name! I shall call you Joseph from now on." From now on? In five months Golden hadn't sent me there, and now she thinks so much stuff comes twice a week! And yet there *were* innumerable bottles, phials and vials and jars collected on her vanity.

She leaned towards me. My eyes struggled up to meet hers. She smiled. "Come here, Joseph." I inched closer. She reached out and took my hands in her cool, red-lacquered, long-nailed fingers; large fingers and strong they were, too. "Let me look at you." She looked into my eyes. I couldn't really see hers, I was so confounded by their

painted sheen and by her suffocating scent, which I could distinguish, now that I was so close, from the fulminating odoriferousness of her . . . boudoir.

"Yes. Yes," she breathed. Yes what? I asked myself.

"Would you like some cake and milk, Joseph?" she said abruptly.

"No, Madame . . . Thank you, but I am obliged to eat my supper later, or my father will be angry." As if from nowhere, how such words evoked themselves formally in response to her!

"Yes, Joseph, of course." She kept hold of one hand as she swivelled again, the kimono sliding down one white and blinding shoulder, reached into the drawer and pulled out a dollar bill. I thought it was a twenty-dollar bill at least, and said, "I don't have change, Madame, I'm afraid, for twenty." Then I realized that Golden had never mentioned any price for the order. "Besides, I forgot what it costs."

"Never mind," she said, "Mr. Golden charges me later. This is for you, Joseph, for coming and for being so sweet." And she folded my fist on the dollar, the biggest tip for the least running I'd done since beginning to work. This was more like it.

"Thank you, Madame, thank you

very much." But she had not freed my hand. I wanted to take it back, but she drew me gently closer, and before I could guess what was happening, she placed my hand inside her kimono, upon her breast. I felt the mole I had already glimpsed, and knew how much I had desired to touch that tiny stipple. A shiver of satisfaction riffled down my neck. "Do you feel, Joseph, how my heart beats?" Surely it was, and I thought I detected it, pulsing there, somewhere. She moved my hand upon her cool skin, over the large, satin-soft nipple. "So, so," she whispered, "gently, Joseph, gently." My hand fostered and led implacably here and there around her breast, shown how to cup and stroke, began to caress her on its own. When she squeezed it against her breast in a hard, involuntary spasm, I discovered that my head ached, and coloured lights burst like pinwheel rockets inside my tightly shut eyes. Then, before I could move, she was working deftly at my clothes, un-buttoning them, pulling at my sleeves—so many sleeves! and at my clumsy legs. In a few minutes I was hot and dry and stiff and naked and tingling with chills in that dimmed, purpling, overheated sweet chamber. Her hands went firmly over me, patting, slapping, pinching.

I didn't know what I felt as she worked and whispered at me like a rapt masseuse. Suddenly, her living hand went between my legs. I cried out in joyful pain. "So, Joseph. So," she said. "Come here, Joseph." And still holding me with her hand she walked me to the bed and sat me down. And then, breathing over my face in a steady, sucking hot roar, like a furnace full of red-white coal, she pressed me down. And then, unclasping that hard, golden dragon, she took me inside her cloak. It was dark every-where now. It was stifling so close to her, but she folded me in and coiled around me like an iron serpent. "The Dragon Lady!" I was thinking. "The Dragon Lady!!" Briefly I wondered if I should pretend I was Pat Ryan, or only Terry, his sidekick kid. And as she directed me with caresses and fierce squeezes and constant murmured imprecations in my ear, I decided, doubtfully, for Pat Ryan, because he was black-haired like myself.

It was snowing outside an hour later when, cleaned up and trying manfully to control my tottering walk, I came back to the indifferent, safe, fluorescent glaring and cluttered insanity, that other insanity, of the *Golden Pharmacy*. I couldn't believe I'd been gone so long, though the lapse of time was shown obviously by the change from afternoon sunlight to store-window-lit evening, from clear cold to an inch of flaky, crunching snow. I hadn't thought of an explanation for Golden because I was not yet able to accept the fact that anything had happened. That is probably what saved me from betraying myself by a hesitant flicker of my eyes, or an apprehensive tic of my cheek. But I quite expected to be zeroed and brought to bay against the wall of confession; I even feared I would break down with the first question focussed at me from behind the glare of Golden's accusatorial glasses. After which I would be fired for laziness and incompetence. Golden passed me over, however, with a shaft of raillery that missed its dumb and quivering mark, and let me creep to the cellar to recover myself. My escape was, I granted, sheer, fortunate chance.

He said: "Hey! Look who's here. Joey, where you been in the snow without your coat?"

Stupefied, I answered, "Delivering an order. Not so far."

"Yeh? You know what time it is? Quarter to six. You went out half past four. What kind of delivery is that? Should I pay you wages, Joey? *You're* Joey the firefoot, the efficiency expert?" I looked at him with false amazement.

"But, Mr. Golden, you forgot to put a name on the package."

"So? I gave you the apartment number. Dumbbell!"

"But, Mr. Golden, you never told me there were *four* Number 39's."

"So? You couldn't come back to ask?"

"Well, I figured it would be easier to try a few doors. You know what I mean?"

"So what took you so long?"

"Well—" I paused, and it came to me. "I went to the North Building, and the elevator was out of order. Up and down: six flights! I went to the East Building, and the same notice was up: Not Working. You know?" I was scared; this was going to be too obvious, but I hoped to bore him with tedious detail. Anyhow, that's what I *had* been doing for five months, climbing stairs, and a lot he'd cared. I went into a complete routine, panting out my wanderings, in pantomime, up and down the vastness of *The Alexandria,* and I felt the release of the passion of my accumulated fatigues, and purging of the many disappointments I'd suffered from his clientele of Mrs. Katzes—for they had tired me the way I was worn out now. "And you know something funny, Mr. Golden? I went to the West Building and the elevator there—"

"Joey, Joey, not again. Please! I'm busy. You gave the order? Good. You got a good tip? Yeh? Fine. You're no better than Sam-u-el. Stupid! Why couldn't you pick the right building on the first try? Go away. Don't wear me out. You'll tell me the elevator's broken there, too?"

"Well, as a matter of fact—"

"No, no," and he lifted a mock fist at me, though for a second I thought he meant to strike me in earnest, and I flinched.

"—that one's working." A little truth to season the lies. He let the cuff fall jestingly on my shoulder as I ducked behind him. Affection from Golden? That *was* something. I crept down the cellar steps, relieved that he had not caught me and so thankful for the fatherly blow of blessing that I could have fallen and hugged his knees with mawkish gratitude.

Once below, I sat down at my table, exhausted, and drooped into thoughtless torpor. After a while, I heard a rustle and a slobbering sigh behind the stairs. I went over to look in on Sam-u-el. He seemed to be quite asleep there in his sepulchral shadows. I nudged his foot. He was asleep. I went back. There was further rustling. A match was struck and flickered momently; some puffs of smoke drifted out and

thinned through the basement. I watched the vapour dissolve in the stillness.

"Joey?"

"Yeah."

"Didja go up there?"

Putting on an annoyed, gruff voice, I said, "Of course! I had to—you didn't want to go. Why not?" He did not answer my question.

"Didja see the tickler?"

"What?"

"You know, the tingaling?"

"What?"

"Ah, come on, fella. You can't be that dumb. Did she show you the twitcher, fella? It's full of teenchy little teeth that go chip-chop! like in a chicken's mouth. They grind together, sorta—you know?" He let loose that scoffing giggle of his. I was mortified. What did he know about it? I was sick with sudden anger against the little beast. I got up ready to kill, and strode over to him. But then I controlled myself, partly because I was ashamed for her sake, whoever she was, at her being in the lurid thoughts of this Sam-u-el, this thing, and partly because I was frightened by what had happened to me up there. "You pissy little pyoick," I growled, "Shut your ignorant mouth or I'll—"

"What?" he laughed.

I gave him a good kick in the

leg. He yelped, and began crying like a girl. I was glad he had the sense to keep it low. I ran upstairs, shut the door tight, and clerked away my hour.

During the next two weeks I began to feel oppressed by the coming on of the future. I didn't know why this sorrow crept over me, but it was dreadful. I had a dream that I was roaming down an endless narrow street flanked by endlessly tall, featureless buildings, their even rows of opaque windows concealing menace; they were buildings without entrances; forward was the only direction I could go. What I feared, I realized in the morning, was that I might be sent to Number 39-South again, and that it was just a matter of time. And, while I waited to go, I dreaded even more what I would face at my return, Sam-u-el's cruel jibes, the mockery of that foul mouth dribbling dirty words expressive of the distorted, livid images he constantly held before his eyes, and the dirty laughter that made my uncertain limbs shudder, not in recollected pleasure, but in eager, empty lust, as if I were recently dead yet wanted to walk abroad again. I was sure he knew nothing of what I had done; his questions were off the track and revealed themselves as guesses and mere ugly imaginings of besotted, private gratifications. Yet he knew enough from his maniacal, self-involved and self-abusive lechery to make me feel in my own fancies as bestial as he, and make me hate myself as much as I did him, as if I were some untarnishable metal subjected, for spite, for aimless folly's sport, for nothing at all, to an unbearable green flame. He grasped that reaction at once, and teased and tortured me by obscene remarks and grotesque gestures. When these were not enough to please him, he took to planting his fetishes and his wastes for me to stumble on or open everywhere—pictures, cigarette butts, condoms blown up like balloons and lettered with foul words that were disfigured by expansion, and so on and on. I began to call myself the ·innocent and blameless and ideal-loving Dr. Jekyll, and him Mr. Hyde, my shambling, bloated, irrepressible, irresponsible and unappeasable, monstrous shadow. In that narrow space in which my working life of suffering mortgaged hours was spent, I had no way to escape him, to hide from that homonculus Mr. Hyde. Late in the days, when I'd had about what I could take, he would let up his jeering and jibing: he saw just how to keep his game going. I was caught—but good.

You would have thought Sam-u-el knew every bit of that Frederick March - Mary Pickford picture; knew how Mr. Hyde's brutish psyche, clothed in its ghastly physical emanation, gradually took over and dominated the idealist Dr. Jekyll; knew how it ended; Dr. Jekyll's committing suicide to escape. The comparison was close enough to occur to me, but too disgusting, and too painfully complex to contemplate. But it kept coming back, no matter how hard I tried not to think of that fog-obsessed, night-obscured 19th Century London, the horror in each Limehouse lane and blind alley. How I longed for escape!

Before the month was over, the cause of my anxiety became real, originating in the same events as before. Sam-u-el refused to go up; so Golden sent me. I wished he would reflect, recall how long it had taken me last time; I wished he would give me warning, better still, an express command to come right back—some pretext to protect me. But he picked a slack hour to make up the stuff and ship it by me, saying only, "You know the way now?"

Again, I had to ring twice; again, I found my way down that simple maze of foyers; again, I stood at the door of her bedroom.

She must be in there. The water stopped. Was she getting out so soon after calling to me to enter or just stepping in? "Joseph?" I didn't reply. "Joseph, come here." Her voice, cajoling, brought me helplessly across the room.

"Come in, Joseph." I walked into a cloud of lavender steam. She was in the tub, behind frosted glass that went nearly to the ceiling. "Sit down."

"Madame, I'm sorry. I must go back. I'm busy. I have orders to return . . . right away."

"Yes? Sit down, Joseph. Keep me company—for just a little while?" What could I do? I wanted to stay. I took off my warm leather coat, which I'd put on to challenge Golden's questioning eyebrow, and also because I'd thought in a muddled way that I'd need a uniform, some sort of armour to indicate to her when she opened the front door that I was busy in the cold streets, full of orders and urgency, that I couldn't possibly linger. I looked hard through the glass encasing the tub, hoping to see where her dark regal head was, but distinguished only a mass of foam moving and making languid, washing, dripping, soaking, fuzzy noises. Her voice in this closed, tiled chamber was not the same as the Dragon Lady's. It was bright, though still sweetly low and cooing; younger perhaps, or sprightlier. In a way, I was happy not to have to look at her. She must have known that, because she took the advantage to ask me questions: how old I was; where I went to school; how I liked working for Mr. Golden; why I worked so hard; what I did with the money I earned; where my father was, what my mother was like. Finally, so flattered was I by her interest, and so curious to delay and maybe see her get out of the tub, I revealed to her what my movie schedule was—what day I went to the *Royal,* what afternoon to the *Imperial,* how I treated myself on Sunday to the *Paradise.* When she asked me to repeat that last one slowly, I was immediately sorry I'd told her. She sat up then, and I saw I'd been talking to the wrong side of the tub. Her blurry form began soaping. She told me to leave my package on the bed and take a dollar from the vanity table. There was a bowl on it full to the brim with fresh quarters and halfdollars, straight from the bank they looked. She called out, "Joseph, goodbye. And come again." Come again? Did that mean, when I was sent, or should I just come? How could I do that? *Come again.* Not me! Lingering at the bedroom door, I heard her open the glass gate. She

sighed deeply. I saw her bending over, completely enwrapped in a white terrycloth robe and hood. As she straightened up, the hood slipped from her head. This woman's hair was short and brown and wavy; I thought I saw a snubby, pert profile, a small mouth, perhaps freckles. She was humming a gay swing number. I dashed fleeting out on tiptoe. I certainly would *not* come back.

There was no need for that. Two days later, right in the middle of the crisis of a risky misadvised safe-cracking job, when a light had to be used and the alarm, set off by accident as in a nightmare, was bling-banging away, and you could just make out the siren wailing in the distance, and the most important tool in the kit turns up missing, someone sat down next to me. I knew who it was by that velvet, soft and seizing perfume. I tried to concentrate on the work in hand. This was the moment when months of planning should pay off, I knew, because the action was not much different from a hundred jobs like this in a hundred other films, except for the precise details: they'd be surrounded: that weak character they shouldn't have taken along (the skinny guy with the sweatful, hollow face and the hacking cough) would be shot down making it to the car; the grey geezer would manage to scramble in the last instant, leaving the door flapping open dangerously; the tough guy would curse through compressed lips frayed with cigarette shreds, and reach out, deadpan, slamming it closed while spraying the coppers; the fat fool would be driving with wild skill and tenacity, revealing an unexpected potential for heroism (which explained why he had been included in the venture), and the calm grim hero, though he had a couple of desperate slugs in him and was bleeding from the mouth, would be in the front seat directing the driver and keeping himself conscious through sheer guts . . . and then the improbably successful getaway, followed by complex evasive manoeuvrings as the gang broke up and quarrelled tragically over the distribution of the loot. Yet those varied details of the hackneyed story—this brave one's flicker of yellow fear, that one's impassive, brainless courage in defiance of stony law, the other's long-expected stool-pigeon quailing in the clutch—these were the touches that mattered, and I always watched for them as if they were omens and I a diviner entrusted with the fate of the city. However, her perfume put me off the film's track, and I sank into it like a patient into undesired anesthesia, fighting for my life—realizing at the same time how helpless I was without an irrelevant cliché such as this one from my concise encyclopedia of movie clips—fighting for my life against the enchanting, mad doctor who intends to practice the strangest surgery on me. Far off, the coppers' tommy guns were counterpointing with their vivid life-like midnight sharp brasses of the tumid score as I turned away to look at her. She was watching the screen, wide-eyed and youthful, a bobbed and banged, chestnut-haired sweetheart, an ingenue. I saw a small, round, brown head, a tan polo coat worn on the shoulders, a pink cashmere sweater moulding her chest. Still, I couldn't have been positive who she really was except for that spiced and oily perfume, and her ears: large, deeply convoluted ears whose lobes seemed an inch long, and were pierced and stretched like a bellybutton's gash by heavy earrings. Though these signs woke in me that anxious distraction I knew her by, I had to be sure, and there was not enough light from the crime-black screen.

So I put my hand out, accidentally, where I hoped hers would be on the arm. It came alive, clawed and ringed as soon as I touched it, and grappled mine like a peregrine's swift talon. Caught! A laughing whisper, "Hello, Joseph. Surprised?" She transferred her other hand to mine, put the near hand up on my thigh and held me fast and cunningly. I couldn't hope to think about the rest of my picture. In the parts I wanted to watch hard, she would be tickling my ear, whispering I don't know what; in the romantic, boring part, when the hero was being nursed back to health in the country by his moll (still hemorrhaging, however), and the farmer's daughter falls for him and they walk and talk by moonlight, she leaned back intent and silent, sucking her lower lip, watching as if I wasn't even there—just at the time I, moviebug though I was, would have been happy to be disturbed. I couldn't take it; she had spoiled the movie. I wanted to cut out and go home. I rose but she pulled me down. "Joseph, will you come with me? Please." Was she asking or telling me?

"No, I don't know who you are. And besides, I have to go home."

"You haven't seen the whole show yet, so you don't have to go home. Anyway, if you are not sure, why not come and find out? Please?" What the hell did she mean? I had only meant to be polite when I said I didn't know her: I had just got that line from the stenographer in the D.A.'s office who was being picked up by the fast operator, the one with the Menjou moustache. It didn't seem I could say an original word to her, I had so many rotten used scripts to refer to, though I had already noticed she never responded logically to the gambits I threw out, but seemed to have another set of lines in mind. I knew I had no control over the situation.

Stalling, I said, "Where can I go with you?"

"Why not try *The Alexandria?* Number 39-South." With that, she chirped coquettishly, let go my leg and arm, and disappeared.

I sulked in my seat for a few more vapid scenes. Finally I got up determined to go home, or something. That something took me straight around to 39-South. I rang the chimes twice; fast. No answer. I tried the knob. Open as before. I didn't quite like the feel of the whole thing, and registered this doubt to myself in the voice of the ancient crook warning the impulsive, young, ambitious gangleader (son of the ambushed master-hijacker). My reservation and my rash resolve both resulted from having been so rudely awakened by her handy presence from my meditative exercise, of having stepped out into the still daylit street long before my customary hour, and of my unauthorized presence here on this day—after all, I had nothing to deliver. Shaking the sage one's apprehensive head, I went on in. I crept cautiously towards her bedroom. No one was there. I peeped into the bathroom, and to make it complete, into the empty, spotless and featureless bedroom of the master of the house, whoever he was. I had halted, puzzled, oscillant between fearless youth curious to find out and heavy experience nervous to clear out, when I was startled by a blast of jazz music from the living room. I raced back down the long foyer, a route I knew by now, having unwillingly traversed it in my mind many times during the last month, sort of practising my lam. Nobody was there either; the console roared. I stood there for a moment, and I lost my chance.

She came jitterbugging in from a door at the opposite end of the room, carrying a round plastic green tray with two abominably tall glasses of milk and a couple of giant chunks of chocolate cake. It was Jean Arthur, slightly youthful: curly, light brown hair, white socks and brown-and-white saddleshoes cutting the rug, a short tartan kilty whose accordion pleats ballooned way out as she swirled, showing off white, tight panties. Her pink cardigan came down on her hips; it was open at the top where a round dickey blouse collar came cutely out. She had three or four ropes of fake-looking pearls on her neck, and fat pearls hanging like weights from her ears; she had lots of orange rouge, and orange, cupid lips.

"Come on, Joseph, let's dig it," she cheered as she slopped the tray down on one of the fancy leather endtables and came bouncing, lindying at me. I didn't think I could ever dance like that.

"I'm sorry," I said stiffly, "I don't dance."

"Oh yes you do! C'mon, let's try." She tugged me stumbling down the wax-glossy steps, tore off my leather coat, and put me into her routine, letting up from the frantic jittering for a few seconds only while the records changed. In a short time, trapped into that frenetic whirl, and glad not to be too close to her dazzling, glass-bright and round Betty Boop eyes, I picked up her beat and capered about as she wished. When the player stopped, I sank to the floor. She skipped away to turn the stack of records over, and I glanced at her narrowly. Was *that* the Dragon Lady? Only, perhaps, in the muscled calves and too-full hips, the sinewy, long-nailed and orange-tipped fingers, the thickish, square shoulders. I thought — I couldn't tell what. The noise crashed on again; she yanked the drapes to, throwing the room into dusk, and came back and sat down with me, her legs drawn up in front of her so she could hug her smooth, tanned shins and rest her cheek coyly on her knees. She made me drink the milk and fed me the chocolate cake, eating fast herself. As soon as that refreshment was done with, I mumbled some words about goodbye, but she jumped to her feet, laughing a shrill, girlish, silver laugh, and held me down. I had no speech for her; none was necessary. Tapping her foot and swaying her skirt to the beat, she sang to the Benny Goodman record playing now,

"Joseph, Joseph,
Won't you make your mind up?
Joseph, Joseph,
I'm in love with you . . ."

Then she flung herself, squirming and jumpy like a fevered filly, upon me. And only then did I feel for sure who she was: it was no girl's light and bicycling body upon me, but that compulsive, channel-swimming, woman's strength.

"Joseph, Joseph," she hummed as she swept over me, "You remember now, don't you?" I did; yet I couldn't accept my former fantasy (it came to me, all right) that I was Ryan, or rather, young Terry now, lost in the Western reaches of China and dreaming of cokes in the haystack with Mary Ann Jones back in the heart of Iowa in harvest moon time. If I wasn't Terry, then who? Swinging there on the thick, spongesoft carpet to the rhythm of Ziggy Elman's trumpet, that nutty Yiddish jazz which filled the whole banal Bronx with its wild screech, I began to think that, maybe, in the end, I was truly her "Joseph, Joseph."

For the next two months, this heavy, jangling, voracious woman intruded herself into my only life; she sought me out in the *Royal,* in the *Imperial,* and on Sunday, in my last refuge, the *Paradise,* where the downtown shows played, and where I hoped that the crowd would hide and defend me from her. Yet no matter how I slouched into the shadow of my seat, or what uncomfortable and awkward angles in back, on the extreme sides or down at the distorted front I chose, sooner or later she would arrive, that impossible bobby-soxer with jewel-framed, harlequin, Hollywood-blue glasses, her pendulous coral earrings, her silk scarves and pearls and rings, and surround me with nervous rustling and pressings and confusing chatter. She knew nothing about how to watch a movie; she was unaccountably blasé during the hottest Indian chase, asked silly questions about horses and ranches, the aiming and shooting of guns, and about whose side who was on—she was unable to tell the good guys from the mean and bad, indifferent to the problems of heroes—their survival, their honour and revenge—that strung together these axle-creaking and leathery wilderness dramas. She held me down, petting and scratching my thighs, and my head tenderly during the big scenes, just when I needed freedom to feel and thrash and jerk with the showdown fights when they were punching and gouging up and down the saloons, round hotel corridors, through doors and over balcony railings, smashing furniture on each other, hurling bottles through mirrors and windows and demolishing with their falling bodies the most expensive, imported gambling equipment and rare Eastern-style, Wyoming apartments. But whenever there was that dull and silly mush where the man and woman yaketty-yakked about nothings and kissed it up till you wanted to shout a warning, Get out, before they catch up with you! It's a trap—then she watched, half-amused, and made me sit holding my breath, absolutely still and twitchless. And I couldn't

prevent her. How I reviled myself for having blurted out my movie routine to her that afternoon. Yet how should I have known that someone who wasn't interested and couldn't understand would even go to the movies? The worst of it was I had no other times when I could go; and nowhere else to go and nothing to do when I was free.

For two months I persevered, keeping up with the minimal amount of homework in school—how nothing that was—and running my orders and counter silently and efficiently for Golden. I had become a settled little career man for that morose and heedless chief, that arcane, pharmaceutical priest whose presence I tried to avoid by remaining downstairs as long as I could. As for the lousy Sam-u-el –I threatened to bash him if he so much as looked at me. And I persevered with her too, trying patiently to instruct her inattention; although, by letting her stay there in the dark with me (as if I might have done otherwise!) I gave away my mental solaces, my mental furbishings and delights. All for what? Usually, I had to give in, and I did it with bad grace, and follow along to number 39-South, where the afternoons passed with dancing and pauses for refreshments, into that arduous, insatiable and crazy hour of hers in which she took the rest of me away; that hour which seemed never to be led up to directly—unless it was by our ritualized, formal struggle, that apparently coincidental yet mysteriously fatal reacquaintance in the obscurity of my theatres—and which each time, that is, twice a week, and to my utter disbelief, exploded on me after I had closed the door and searched for her as stealthily as I could manage through that apartment in which she always trapped me. And no wonder I couldn't find her first: for when I had passed the cement lions guarding *The Alexandria* my mind stopped grinding; it neither dreamed nor figured but went into a light coma as I moved, automatically quick, towards the correct elevator, punched the button for the sixth floor, and then slunk down the hall to Number 39, where I stopped only to hear her chimes sound up and down, waited, out of courtesy, for an answer which did not come, and then set them off, again to cover my opening and closing of the door.

So our unvarying programme went for eight weeks, and each time it was like going to die. Nevertheless, towards the end of the second month it seemed to me that I was going willingly on my own, for I no longer fretted and fought to delay, making myself repeat garbled, inane equivocations in the attempt to forestall that passionate moment in the movie house when she would whisper, "Joseph? Will you come with me, please?" I found I was waiting for her to press my arm, lean to me and nibble at my ear with those words. In fact, one Thursday, we had hardly gotten through the first reel of the first feature when I wanted to clear out on that sunny, silly, country romance in which Laraine Day was leading on or being led on by some smooth guy—he had the usual creamy convertible coupe and there were studio trees and studio cottages and cardboard moonlight—and I almost told her so. But I couldn't bring myself to it. I brushed my free hand over her wrist. She shook it off. I put it on her knee, modestly, not too high up. Her legs squeezed together rejectingly tight. For an instant, I fancied that this time, it was actually the wrong woman, and made as if to sneak away. Of course it wasn't someone else: who but she would have my hand so locked in hers? I glanced at her; she had on a kerchief which covered her whole head and was tied tightly under her chin and tucked behind into her raised coat collar. I was amazed to see tears furrowing her cheeks and leaving tiny scars of clotted powder and mascara. "What's the matter with you?" I hissed. "This is a silly picture and you know it. The next is the good one." She shook her head. Was she saying she didn't know why she had those tears, or was she angrily asking me to shut up? "Come on, grow up, will you? Crying at this corny crap!" She shook her head again—sadly it seemed—and said nothing. I begged in a whisper, "Ah, please! Cut it out." Her crying made me feel a little hollow in my stomach. "I'm going," I said.

"Wait for me, Joseph, Please!"

"What do you mean, wait for you?"

"Upstairs," she said. Fumbling in her baggy coat pocket, she brought out a key. I took it without even thinking of the next picture, a Humphrey Bogart, which a few weeks earlier I could not conceivably have missed for anything, for anything! But I got up and went out.

I had sworn a lacerating oath not to return to her today, but I ran straight there. And once in, I remembered to leave the door unlatched—my mind was working well now, though on nothing at all —and went to the bedroom. I sat down at her vanity, and started counting her collection of bottles and jars as if their labels, all *Golden Pharmacy,* would spell something for me. It also helped me not to see my face in the mirror: I did not know what expression I might find. But their myriad shapes, qualities and sizes only baffled me. I heard the door open and close far away. How well I had come to know her scurrying saddleshoed step. I looked in the mirror, over my shoulder, as she went by. She held a handkerchief with both hands to her face, which must have been mauled by her tears. She crossed quickly to the bathroom. What *was* the matter with her? The lock snapped, she called, "Joseph, I'm changing. Go out and wait in the parlour . . .Go on!"

I went. I don't want to be here, I thought. I don't! I could still get away safe; I could even hustle back and catch the Bogart film. Yet I wished to stay. I can kill the three hours here, I told myself. What else did my life leave me when I wasn't suffering squalidly at school, brutally busy at the *Golden Pharmacy,* or sleeping and eating like a dead one at home? And I had to concede that, anyway, I should have come after her later on this afternoon, oath or no oath, as soon as she loused up my Bogart.

I went down the hall, opening and shutting all those doors to crowded closets which hid nothing but incomprehensible quantities of costumes, colourful clothes for every season and mood and occasion. In the living room, I pulled out some albums at random and decided on quiet music. I put a pile of records on, foxtrots and tangos, the strings, of Kostelanatz and Gould. I tried to think what she might like, so I drew the drapes to as was customary for that room. March, though still biting cold and wet, was growing brighter, and this early hour didn't go with twilight music. Then I took off my leather coat, plumbed into a corner of the down-pillowed engulfing couch and waited for her appearance.

I don't know how long I waited, because I fell asleep. I awoke, startled by the silence. The last record had played, leaving behind only the faint electronic hum of the speaker. Then, I heard her in the kitchen. Had the noises she made as she worked been in a movie, they would have told me what to expect; nothing in a film surprised me any more, for I was an adept in translating even the title blinking on the marquee into the unreeling simplicities of celluloid fatality. I certainly would have guessed that there were high heels afoot in the kitchen and drinks being mixed. But I had no title to go by, and I felt merely dully real; I didn't discriminate, the sounds. So, when she came through the door, I was smashed into a wonder of speechlessness such as only the unknown and totally unforeseen can cause. Carrying a square silver tray which had on it twin long-stemmed crystal glasses filled with the palest amber fluid just barely bubbling, and a silver cocktail shaker, she was dressed in an evening gown that enclosed her, from her ten gilded toes to just above her formidable breasts, like the cold stalk of an artificial flower. It was a scaly sheath of hammered and sequined gold. Diamond bracelets, or what looked fabulously like diamonds, gauntleted her wrists, and a diamond-glittering, platinum collar yoked her throat. Her sharp, drawn-out nails were goldflecked and her fingers bristled with diamond and topaz rings. I looked down, where her white-ankled foot stepped shyly forward, hobbled, from the short slit in the sheath, wearing a gold-mailed, backless and toeless and spike-heeled slipper; I looked up, and failed to remember her face, for the face I saw was framed by long, thick, straight, golden-white hair, rolled under at the ends. That hair shielding the right half of her face—it was . . . Gloria Grahame . . . versus . . . Bogart? Even her eyes seemed to glow gold, liquid gold as in a fraudulent alchemist's ladle; and her mouth was turned down at the corners in a contemptuous sneer; and there was a bronzeflaked beauty-spot pencilled high on the left cheek. Her radiant perfume preceded her towards me. I had been set to bound away in terror, but that scent I knew; it kept me still. "Joseph? No milk and cake for us this afternoon."

"No milk and cake," I said.

She stopped to place the tray on the morocco-topped cocktail table, hovering voluptuously over it so that I might goggle my fill at this apparition of the svelte where there had been a jitterbug, the sultry, swank and demi-mondaine where I had grown perhaps too familiar with the hot fudge sundae from over the next white picket fence, my elm street and maple avenue American jukebox girl. She pulled a gold-and-silver threaded hassock over and seated herself to face me, her knees almost touching mine, and that so plushly sophisticated and nightclub visage gazing seriously at me. She gave me one of the fragile, diamond-cut glasses, took the other up and, clinking them, said in husky toast, "Joseph, these are champagne cocktails."

"Champagne cocktails."

"Let's drink, my dear Joseph, to our special friendship."

"Friendship," I followed stupidly.

"And drink to us, that we may continue to be loving friends. I don't want to quarrel, Joseph dear."

"Loving friends? Quarrel?"

"Drink up, dear."

She sipped; I drank. My father sometimes let me taste his shotglass of whiskey before Sunday dinner, and it went down like mercurochrome; I'd never tasted anything like this. This was good : sour-sweet, and strong. She opened a little golden casket that lay on the cocktail table and took out a very long cigarette, gold-tipped. I hadn't seen one like it behind my counter at the *Pharmacy,* though Golden said he carried every brand. "These are made to order for me," she remarked. I flicked up the lighter for her, gallant Bogart waiting out the dame to learn what her racket was before he let her have it . . . have what? Well anyway, this sort of glamour is sure to be dangerous; there must be silky crime, money, dead bodies behind every word of hers—that was the notion bubbling through my Bogartish brain. "Do you like it?" The smell of that Eastern tobacco was oil-heavy and plangent with bored lusts; it floated slowly away through the room in thin layers of languid cloud.

"Yes," I said, shrugging. What next, what next! She poured another glass for me, half a glass for herself, and then sat dreaming, sipping, smoking. I couldn't stand to look straight at that solid, utterly new face and hair, so I searched shyly for the mole, the mole I thought I knew, on her breast. It was, I think, still there, though so faint, as if touched by a whitening cream. Okay, your move, baby, I heard him say in my foolish forehead.

"Joseph . . . Joseph, you do love me? You know how I feel about you, don't you?" This vibrant, crooning voice just could not be happening, I thought, not really for *real*. And to myself, I said in warning, None of those corny lines now, and tried to reply.

"Now wait a minute—" Her enormous, phony eyelashes dropped— I hoped she wasn't going to start in crying again, not *this* babe, this babe could take it straight from the shoulder—"Let's be frank with each other. Let's lay our cards on the table, okay?" My God! My God! I kicked myself.

"Yes, Joseph. I know. You don't really love me. And I don't want you to say you do if you don't. I wouldn't want you to lie to me." She put the words in my mouth and then took them right out again. I was lost in her presence, always lost. She was always playing out of bounds. It wasn't fair. What was it I really wanted to say?

"Joseph, you don't really love me, do you?"

"How can I love you? You haven't even told me your name."

"What difference does that make?"

"I don't know. Plenty."

"Don't be silly. We have so much else between us."

"I'd like to know your name, that's all. You see what I mean?" And I confessed what was bothering me: I had too many names for her. I told her that at first I had called her the Dragon Lady. She laughed at that, the low, undecipherable, exotic Dragon Lady laugh. Then I thought I'd known her as The Country Girl; Jean Arthur, Laraine Day, Irene Dunne even. She tittered.

"Are you saying you'd love me, Joseph, if you knew my name?"

"I don't know what you mean."

"Well, just supposing."

"How should I know?"

"Then you won't." She turned her head away. I took hold of her shoulders, quite surprised at myself.

"I will. I will love you. I promise. I do now, right now." I leaned over and kissed her cheek. She sighed, but said nothing. "Well?"

"No you won't want to love me

when I tell you."

I crossed my heart; I held up my hand; I promised over again. She didn't tell me her name. She only turned back to me, strong and fierce and hungry. Her determined mouth had a hundred talents; her lips were creatures possessed; her tongue was a snake, a ship, a battering ram, a flower blossoming red and many-petalled. I tore away and ran to her bedroom. I was beside myself to be back in that deep place her bed again, instead of whomping and rolling around on the floor and over the furniture like kids at a blackout party.

She gave me the wealth of women: various, abundant, sweltering like a fanatic even in this glacial disguise of hers with which she welcomed the mild, modern spring of the treeless Bronx. And, terrified, I responded to her with a lover's filial awkwardness, as if she were all I had to look forward to in life. At first she had overwhelmed my body in a consuming rampage. Then what had been my spiritual food, my ambrosial movies, she had gradually soured, curdled, and then dashed away with her irritating, ignorant attendance at my side, her vacuous erratic attention to the false, her carelessness and lack of interest in cinematic truth, and her banal, undiscriminating enthusiasm

for slush. She did not know how to suck the bones in which I believed the essence of our human existence was concealed; she seemed to want only the diluted juice so easily squeezed from formless fat. To my way of thinking at least, she was fooled by the outward appearance of things, and just like a female, followed and changed with every fashion, adoring and adorning the plastic and perishable body. Now, lacking a will of my own, I'd become the worshipful, worshipping victim of its most paradoxical phase — idolatrous I served the bitch.

But not willingly. The affair, because of her latest incarnation (there was no other word for it), had become too complicated to sustain much longer, too intense, and exhausting. Not physically— she was somewhere between thirty and forty, and I was fifteen, growing fast and full of new, well-exercised muscle—but exhaustive of possibility, so high had the incredible illusion she created been pitched. She had once been that Asiatic temptress, an erotic reptile; and then had abandoned the role for that of my madcap adolescent play-mate, my friendly, sexy little sister, that brown bunny with electric fur hind legs of steel and sharp teeth that could nibble you to death; now she was a woman, the desirable, yielding woman of tender violences, dressed in this hard, most gorgeous costume. True, she'd been driven to it by circumstance—hopeful youth betrayed, given to hard men's use—until by sheer unbreakable drive and ruthless intelligence she had emerged invulnerable; true, she was cut from the domestic poetry of ordinary loving in an ordinary frame house for which she still wistfully longed, but it made her the more valuable and capable when at last she gave herself to a true and innocent lover, myself, the only one who saw the original, virginal she secreted within. It was a pity though, that unlike her magnified silver sisters, she did not intend to die faithfully with me when the gross man who kept her returned from his business trip into the racketeer's outlawed unknown; and a pity that I, who had given up everything I believed in and was for this fatal queen, would have to accept that approaching disaster all by myself. And it was coming to that, even though I was, in my true conceit, furiously unaware of our true situation.

Nevertheless my defect, the astigmatic flaw in my besotted perception, did not derive from this corny and abysmally low scenario I'd concocted to explain what was

happening; it lay in the fact that I too had been driven remorselessly into the last deadened street of self-deception by a disinterested and witty doom. I call it "witty," because I think it worked out to inform me for my own good, the only thing no one sees for himself. For I'd forsaken, many years ago it seemed, my primitive country, where I should have had an eventless evolution, and bound myself to drudging serfdom in the *Golden Pharmacy* for a sufficient reason: the movies alone satisfied my craving for higher knowledge, the deeper experience of that greater civilization that lay beyond the stony nomadry of my brethren of the streets, the Bronx boys. Because of that I had fallen into the hot hands of this multiple, mutable lady who, although she seemed so much like those who governed the destiny of my filmic heroes, was strangely different: for she was both essentially unknowable and grossly real. And when at last she deprived me of the movies, I no longer cared to support with my green strength and principled loyalty Golden's fruitless, commercial necessity. I had nowhere to turn.

And yet if I still went on working at the *Golden Pharmacy*, it was because of her. On one hand I was afraid of having more time to devote to her; on the other, I needed money now to buy the small offerings she didn't want. She repeated every other day that she needed my love, and that I could not bribe her with junk. But I had no way of telling her I loved her except by writing what I considered rather elegant and exact notes of affection, and wrapping them up with the paltry Persian shawls and Indian paisley scarves, the two dollar ninety-five rings, earrings, necklaces, and silver-filigree, chain-linked bracelets I picked out with agonizing connoisseurship at a dingy shop with broken plaster on the walls and a rusty whitewashed flower-stamped tin ceiling, an ex-grocery store down on Tremont Avenue, run by a sallow, haggling Armenian in a wrinkled, black, pinstriped suit. She said these presents and declarations meant nothing; she said she'd know when I loved her truly. I swore at her that I loved her; I tore my hair at her to prove the intensity of my love. In a choking exasperation, one Thursday afternoon, the last Thursday we were together—my bloodsweated gift rejected once more in that stubborn, unbelieving, hard-headed and yet intuitively practical female way—I reached out and slapped her, pretty hard.

"You *know* I love you," I yelled. "I show you I love you! I come to you, I stay with you. I go on working like a dog for Golden. And what do I do—spend it on myself? go to the movies? No—I bring you beautiful jewellery. And you refuse it! What else *can* I do to show you how I love you? You're driving me crazy!" It made no difference to her. She held her hand to her swelling cheek, and smiled at me.

"You shouldn't force yourself, Joseph. You don't love me." Was there no way to demonstrate love to her? I slapped her on the other cheek —harder, backhand, even!—leaning into the blow with all my strength. And then I fell upon her with a frenzied lover's fury. Later, she leaned over me, drooping her hair over my head and kissing my face with feathery kisses, her knee thrown leaden over my trembling things, and her woman's sand-heavy breast resting on my shoulder, "Joseph, I don't want you to force yourself to lie to me. It doesn't matter."

"But it does!"

"Why, Joseph?"

"What am I doing here then?"

"Pleasing me."

"I want to please myself, too."

"Ah, Joseph, don't dream of it. You can't make yourself do that. Believe me, I should know."

"Oh God! What do *you* know?"

She smiled and kissed me again. I lay locked under her. It was no use, even if I burst my heart in anger. I felt like socking her. I looked at her face, blurred and featureless without make-up, her shoulders, not white but yellowing and liverspotted; under my palm I felt a rippling roll of fat on her flank, and the coarse matted hair of her groin. Suddenly, I knew she was right. I gave up. "All right, all right, I'm lying. God damn it, you old bag, you—All right, I don't love you. You're perfectly sure you're so right. Well, you are! I hate you, in fact. I spit on you!" She merely smiled again. Oh that smugness, that condescending mothering wisdom. I struggled to get up.

"Joseph! Don't go."

"You know so damn much? Okay, okay. Choke on that smile!"

I managed to dress without looking at her. But, tying my shoe-laces, I glanced up and saw her quietly watching me. That hard yet famished gaze nearly cowed me, but the smile lingering in the corners of her mouth drove me on. My head was breaking, literally breaking apart with frustrated thought and feeling, hatred and love both wrestling and throttling each other to death inside my head. Not looking at her again, I ran out, leaving my coat behind.

I had no idea why I'd carried it all day, except that I'd started out to wear it in the morning, and then I'd cut school. It was the kind of useless vagary I'd been capable of these last four weeks. Well, I hated that heavy leather coat anyway; it was much too warm to wear now in mid-April, and it attached me to intolerable memories of the whole winter past, which I regarded as a season of most hideous suffering, happy though I'd believed myself to be all along. "Good riddance!" I raved back over my shoulder as I slammed into the elevator, "good riddance! You can keep it for all I care!"

Yet I didn't actually believe it was the end. I was dying only to get out of *The Alexandria* and walk, walk anywhere until it was time to go home to wash and dress up. That night the holidays were beginning: my father, and all the other fathers, would be home early for a change, and we'd go up to my grandparents, where the clan would trek in from all over the Bronx and Brooklyn for the annual feast commemorating deliverance by the Angel of Death, the only person in the Passover ritual I liked besides poor, frozen-faced Pharaoh who couldn't seem to help his accursed spite. When the elevator jerked to a stop, I threw open the door and bumped right into Golden. Behind him was Sam-u-el.

Golden grabbed my arms. "Hey, hey! Look who's here! Joey, you don't live here." I was astonished, but still coherent enough to say nothing. "What are you *doing, here?*"

"A friend—I got a friend in this building."

"Yeh? Sam-u-el, you know his friend?" What was he asking that loathsome little bastard for? He knew we didn't talk to each other; he knew I hated him, I'd as much as told him so. Indeed, what were *they* doing here? It hadn't come to me yet, the answer, but it would soon. Sam-u-el, standing well behind Golden's thick back, sneered, "He's got a friend here, all right."

"Yeah? How would you know, you filthy pyoick, you!"

"Hey, hey, Joey!" Golden admonished, as between kids quarrelling.

Then Sam-u-el yapped, "Smell him, smell him, Uncle Eli! Smell him! Go on, smell him!"

Golden held me tighter and sniffed at my hair. I couldn't resist him; I was limp with confusion.

"So, Joey? You got a friend, yeh?" Now I *was* scared. Golden his uncle? So that was why he'd hired him and stood for his crap!

I was beginning to understand. "Come here, Joey. Yeh?" Sam-u-el had already dodged behind me to hold the elevator open, and Golden backed me in and pressed me against the wall. Sam-u-el pushed 6, and stood there with his brown-coated tongue out at me, mocking, "Nyaa! Nyaa! Nyaa! until Golden told him to shut up. I was quaking now. The unbelievable was happening and I couldn't think what would come next although surely, surely, I must have seen it.

"Mr. Golden, Mr. Golden, let me go," I said, mustering a stern indignation. "I have to go home. What do you think you're doing? You can't do this to me. You're crazy. You can't get away with it. What's the matter with you, you listen to that dirty Sam-u-el?"

"Yeh, Joey? Let's see, no?" He backed me down the long corridor quickly, never relaxing his grip on my arms. I stumbled and hopped backwards to stay on my feet. I think he would have been glad to stomp right over me if I'd fallen. Sam-u-el opened the door: number 39-South, and Golden called out, driving me steadily back down the long foyer, "Hey! Goldie! You're home, Goldie?" I could see Sam-u-el's unspeakable face, grimacing with glee, bobbing behind Golden's shoulders, right then left.

Golden shoved, paying no attention to me, as if I happened just to be in his way, and mattered nothing to him.

When we all tumbled into her bedroom, there was another surprise waiting. The place was a mess; it looked as if there had been a real movie struggle in it; whereas when I'd run out five minutes before only the velvet bedspread lay thrown in a heap on the floor and only the bed itself had been upset. Then there was an anguished, rising and falling wail from the bathroom, and she emerged from it holding my leather coat before her like a trophy. I could have been ready to protest with my life that it was another woman I saw. Barefoot, she limped out, squat-looking in a pink chenille housecoat which was ripped apart under the left armpit, a full-length, awfully pink thing she clutched together heedlessly at the waist. That glittering platinum hair which had electrified me when I first saw it was savagely disrepaired, straggling and hanging down every way, as if she was a mourner who had been tearing at that splendid coiffure. And her face, mottled with purple blotches of emotion, was swollen worst where I'd struck her cheeks. And her blank, streaming, redshot eyes. And that greasy cold-creamed skin, going

dead, in which, even from across the room, I saw that Mrs. Katz's wrinkles would be graven in ten years' time . . . I didn't know that contorted face. Her voice shrieked hysterically, a pushcart harridan's. "You caught him? Good. Kill him, the dirty *schvantz,* the little bastard. "Kill him! Kill him!"

Level and judicial, he said, "Goldie, what's the matter now?"

"What's the matter? What's the matter? Where do you get these boys! He comes in here like he has an order for me. He doesn't bother himself ringing. Just because I gave him cookies and milk once, he acts like he lives here—he comes right into the bedroom. Did you ever hear of such a thing? I never!"

Sam-u-el collapsed against the wall by the door, cackling. What the hell was so funny?

"Yeh, Goldie? Joey, you came here today? Why? What happened, she called you?"

I was about to take my chance and say Yes, when she started ranting again. "Kill him—or kill me! So help me, I'll die! Look at me, Golden!"

"Goldie, let him—"

"I was resting. I was taking a nap—I can't even nap without your kids coming in, Golden—and there he is. Not enough he's got no business here, he wakes me up.

You know I need my rest. And, look at this place! Just look! He—that *schvantz,* that little bastard—he jumped on the bed with me. He—he—he tried to—Golden, Golden, I can't say what happened."

"Yeh?" Golden rattled me so hard my joints cracked.

"Mr. Golden, I swear I—"

"You shut up!" she howled. "He'll fix you: he'll kill you. You, you—! Don't leave him for the police, Golden. What he did to me! Look at this place, look what he did to my room."

"Wait a minute, Goldie. You're sure you—"

"Sure? Sure I'm sure! Am I crazy, Golden, you fat pig, you stupid ass! Move already! Look, I held on to his coat when he tried to get out. So? What's his coat doing here?"

Sam-u-el was gagging laughter. "Oh! Oh! Oh! Oh! Oh!" This was a madhouse!

"Now, Goldie, Joey's a clean boy, I tell you. I know him. Even if his coat . . ." He looked at me with those weak grey eyebrows of his raised, not, as I'd always thought, quizzically, but puzzled. He was pretty slow, after all. I saw now that he didn't think his way through things, but felt, gropingly, painfully, afraid to step, yet impelled to, by squealing, squalling, screaming voices on every side of him. He was not the prescient wizard compounding cures for everybody, but a sorrowing, confused old chemist; rich, yes, but merely a servant ministering impartially, for good money, to the vital and the trivial needs of a clamouring world at large. Poor Golden! Poor, betrayed Golden. There were more sides to it than I had ever imagined. "Goldie," he sighed, and took a timorous breath, "Maybe you—?"

"Oh, my God in Heaven, Golden, I'll die of shame from you! Look at me, will you! What more do you want? Look at that nephew of yours, just look at that little animal! He's like the rest of you. Oh, I'll die, I'll kill myself. I swear it! I'll kill myself right now! Golden!"

"Joey—?" Patiently, Golden was beginning again, "Joey, you—?" But she threw herself shrilling upon me. She smelled terribly, sweaty and musty: it was not her smell. Seizing my face between her strong hands, she ripped at both my cheeks. I yelped with the pain of it. Though she wasn't the woman I had known, those were certainly her proud, raking nails.

"Goldie!" He let go of me and ran clumsily after her to the bathroom. But she'd slammed the door in time. She was in a fury. "I'll kill myself. It's too late, Golden, you

132

pig! I can't stand it anymore. I swear I'll kill myself!" she wept from behind the locked door. There was a fearful crashing of glass.

"Goldie!" he roared in misery, "Goldie, open this door!"

I bolted, halting long enough at the other door to bash that Sam-u-el right on the top of his crooked, cheesy skull, muttering, "For you, you—!" As I went past him, he stuck his foot out. Sprawled on my face, I heard his mean laugh behind me. I scrambled up. Down the foyer and out the door I went, leaping the cheap marbled flights of stairs, three steps at a time, and hurdling bannisters wildly until I came out into the *The Alexandria's* meagrely leaved, drab courtyard.

A pale afternoon sun warmed the sky. The local flock of pigeons, startled by my headlong flight, scattered fluttering round the quadrangle, and a burst of sparrows chattered in the shabby untrimmed privet hedges. Outside on the street, cars and delivery trucks passed in their usual traffic. Some little girls were playing hopscotch at the archway, and a couple of little boys leaned on the handlebars of their bikes, watching them skip through the chalked-out and numbered potsy squares. Nothing much was doing, as usual. Breathing in my panic like a broken-winded runner, I made

for the cement lions, but had to stop short. I had a stitch in my side. My face smarted. I put my hands up to wipe my burning sweaty cheeks, and cried out from the pain. It wasn't sweat but sticky blood that covered my face. That horrible cat had gashed me. Blood was dripping on my shirt; now that I had noticed it, my face began throbbing and flaring with the etching fire of pain. Yet now I was laughing too. My blind fear was melting in laughter and tears and blood. I realized I was free. I was free!

THE TRIAL OF GRETCHEN GREEN
by NAZLI NOUR

Dragged down steps / *Let me go* /
by four masked policemen /
struggled dressed body—

Hands grew deeper into / thick
forest / Gretchen twenty /

out stepped / deliberately / express
remaining sense freedom / against
masculine force
it's just ridiculous she said
I mean what have I done wrong?
silence crashed in / behind
walked / guarding / possible
escape—

Miss, remember everything taken

down and used in evidence
A dragonfly flew / words
against you clipped mind / tossed
head / broken cobwebs into
space / flapping thin wings—

*I hate creepy crawlies and flying
things like that* trying explanation
Hate creepy crawlies voice
policemen—

*Do you really take down…a waste
of time…just damn stupid*
clasped wrists / in / marched
Squeezing / brambles / trees far
thick / got Gretchen through bird
efforts / leaves piled thick closely
woven past seasons / stuffed warm
insects hovered everywhere / in
freedom / out wild flowers / grass
stood growth—

But where are you taking me?
heart beats / grew darker /
policeman coughs in silence *You
can't take me like this* stop steps
*Kidnapping…you won't get away…
you won't* screwing teeth up /
with them *There* spat unmilky
ice cream drop—

Spat—Rogon—take down
unrestrained his anger—
*Are you taking me? answer me…
answer ground…answer me…*
fierced *There* gave hard / to
policemen—

Ooowaa…kicked…down Rogon hide
pain / jumping pelican—

I hate you men tree tops / now
filled swarm / creaking black
birds / earth red stony /
atmosphere / haunting terror /
terrible unexpectancy / round
each / hardly see them / held her
wrists / glad in some way—

I'm frightened half whispered
I don't like dark huge toad
stares / mud blob / up—

like the dark voice behind her—

*I don't like it…I hate it…at
least take down what I say
correctly* mild voice / not wanting
upset / case / alone *let me hold
your hands…won't run away*
trying to see faces / semi-
convincingly / thought passed
through / easier / fear dark /
brought thought to a close—

*Trying to flirt…they like to
know about* shriek of some birds /
high up attics—

Flirt howled *Flirt with you lot…
thousand pounds* arms body /
policemen / on her-wind suddenly
rose / themselves down step
bank / Gretchen silk white dress /
round cling / out sea shape /
became shadow / sound water
fall / ran ears *water…are you
going to drown me?* fear / crept—

Suspicion…down as well Rogon
policemen front / statement—

It's hopeless in despair / strong
light pushed forth / greater ease /
faces form / policemen—*your
faces are pink* overflowed black
masks / heavy sneeze / walked
blue bell path. *I shall tell…
newspapers… listen…ring up…
radiomen…about you television
men…everybody will…see…
friends…there are important
people…don't think going away…
lightly*
bluttered / great speed anger—

Revenge…got Rogon wisely—

Revenge…it will be more trying /
push / nightmarish fever—

Crispy cold / grass tinted white
frost net / flower closed petal /
door faces / from dark eyes / trees
white veined *It's snowing snow all
the way* bewilderment *it's
summer—it was mid-summer this
afternoon…it's mad we haven't
been walking that far* looked
around / make sure / white cold
*But it can't be winter suddenly
like this—it can't* shivered / sign
comfort / silence—

To set…note Rogon reflection—

Oh shut up I'm cold skin sprang
out / attack bone / metal in the
skin *what's that light over there?*
light began / bigger brighter as
they neared in *can't see…have you
a pair of glasses sun? I want a*

pair

Greed calling out numbers /
lottery game—

*Yes I found it…all escaped a
luny bin…planned a four man rape*
shrieked / long ice / voice *False
accusations* policemen *dirty mind*
murmured Rogon—*Will be in all
the newspapers…world…film…
century…won't let you get away*
said fighting against / uniform
march—

Blackmail sniggered / pen book—

Forest critical silent / intense /
tried gently hip / hard thigh
policemen on left *Oh let me go
back…I'll give anything you want…
rich people would reward you…big
mansions…cars…servants…any want*
smiled humbly—

Anything wanted repeated /
holding. *Temptation…temptation*
roared / fury hearing weakness /
*No…No…that's not all…if you let
me go…I shall let one of you
marry me…make love to me*
blanked *Make love to me…
Make love to…Make love…Make*
shrieked out / chorus grunt
groans—

Burst tears / reality said / tore
stomach / vomit self up / as pink
flesh / wrinkled feature / broke
life lines—

Seducing...seducing roared Rogon /
   wild pigs broke / white silence
The ice is melting...worse

nightmares...will earth melt too?
laughter sprang trees / Gretchen
jumped *who's that...ice...gone to
sand...trees turned to sunflowers...
what world is?* hard paw banged /
head round / like captured horse
*A pig... a man...a pig dressed in a
morning suit* out leaves fell
down / autumn storm / yellow
brown light / the days past / of
past—

You're mad...who are you with
air / snapping space / crashing
rockets / small like rain—

*You're mad...who are you with
such a face?* looked / they too /
accompanied capture / pink
faces / turned up noses / small
eyes / *I thought you were men...
but you are just pigs...my father
is good friends with the butcher...
he specializes in pigs...*they will
kill you all...sausages *of...for the
masses* stamping her protest /
front / half dozen pigs / in vast
green palm leaves / tails dangling
soft breeze—

Gretchen Green said pig / hard
*bring her nearer added Men...they
could not possibly be men...
I prefer to die than any of you
make love to me* out /

remembering terrible offer—

Shut up woman abruptly / sat
palm leaf / playing sand around /
with dirty hooves—

*His Highness will be here in a
moment* added burp
Which Highness? echoed
rainbow / line waves—

Never you mind...just keep quiet
fastened sleep lumps / sly corner
eyes—

*I will not...if I don't want to...be
bossed around by pigs* answered
pride / look down / sitting—

Police another charge / noted *get
the bramble sticks* passed
around / shouted *the tiny split
ones* ran behind big mushroom /
two-legged pigs—

What for stepped back *you dare
try hit me...I'll tell man coming...
Highness* nobody replied /
talking selves / tried understand
another language / caught hold /
unfamiliar words...locka hooka
banka-splished luti luma *What are
you saying?* may be terrible crowd
pigs standing / mauve mushroom /
whispering *All this hanging...
nobody knows where I am...just
think I didn't want life* thoughts
drew round circles / in sand spin /
round on *strange pond...as if I the
stone...raindrop within whirl* tried

bend / authority—

Brambles ready shouted reading /
mushroom / pig behind—

*Bring…his Highness will be in
3mins 25seconds…is everything
ready* directed hoof scrambles—

*Tunnels…deep dark in earth…fall
in…never climb out* muttered / in
3mins 25seconds…what? took mind
from whirls—

Thunder broke / superimposed
gong bells / palm leaves rose /
pigs / wagged tail / costumes
black—

He is rising came general uproar
thunder his Highness—

*What…look earth beyond is
cracking…opening…swallow* terror /
gesticulating / sight / huge
avenue / so long end / mist like
horizon sea / side lined with
voluptuous apple trees / firing
red leaves branches out / sound
big heavy boots / clamping
weight / towards *Who's coming…
old man / …be big…get me an
apple…I'm hungry* called through
oxygen / clouds / came vast man
pig / twice size / big golden metal
ring hanging round nose / wore
striped trousers / tailed black
jacket / top hat with large zebra
snake / curled walk on serious
face *Is that him?…he is not*

*different from being the Highness…
but he has a snake* thunder /
stopped over erected blue hills /
bells went on ticking / stereopho-
nic clocks / up air change—

Welcome your Highness chorused
grunt / claps jigs—

Is she here? firmly deep voice /
arrived sand—

Yeh…Sir tripping / blushing red
skin—

Thankyou cigar marble case /
already lit / took smoke
*Hmmm…Hmm Gretchen Green…
I—bring her nearer… listen
carefully* policemen pushed
force near Highness / handing
written book—

*Notes…those pigs took down all
wrong… / sshh… no comments
Gretchen…where are the brambles?*

asked Highness seated / turned
pigs bringing / thin corn / bramble
sticks *You dare* eyed / electric
defence lines / to Highness—

Gretchen Green opened pages
this is you clearing voices /
organ pipe / throb heart /
frantically echoed forest—

Ooh…my heart…my mind wailed
suffering rhythm / heat / pigs sat
attentively concert hall—

Hate creepy...said Highness /
commandments—

Well I...*voice defending* to tropical
lands / transparent / swollen
criss-cross / wanting death /
thrashed her legs / into weak
blurred blankness / stared
swelling / glassy flight birds /
to sun stomach / hours ever /
swayed / faint breath / falling
no...*no*...*I didn't want*... *eyes like*
dying fish...*could no longer see*...
distant land body...*in flying air—*

Seducing...*seducing* said voice
Highness / close note book / men
nodded heads / mop brows
Bring her to me got up / adjusted
waistcoat / snake on hat /
upright / whirled zebra face into
space / policemen dragged
Gretchen along sand / legs
bleeding cuts / hair wet / flowed
wind / body moist / to circle
pigs / Highness / dumped at his
feet / lying stomach / on grains /
flesh *Get some apples* rushed /
flaming burn out / pockets /
silenced pigs / grabbed back—

Here your Highness whispered
squeeze them on her face
ordered between hoved hands /
juice drop / sweet rain / curving
cheeks / along eyes down /
open lips / opened looking his
face / new air oxygen / smiled /

Highness / took ring from his
nose / slid ring on her finger /
golden sand / grey-mauve mist /
flew from green-blue mountains /
yellow hot *You are married* said
whispering ear / lifted abandoned
body / into arms / he walked /
long avenue / pigs followed
behind / leaves wedded /
water fall sides / into opening
closing sun...

THE TICKET THAT EXPLODED
by WILLIAM BURROUGHS

With bitter hilarity William Burroughs blasts our mismanaged and degraded planet. The section printed here is a continuous excerpt from his latest novel, The Ticket That Exploded. *Readers unfamiliar with Burroughs' fold-in technique of writing may appreciate the author's explanation of what he's about: "My writing methods are similar to those of photographic montage. I want some of my characters in focus and others out of focus. So I cut into the story with a flash-forward in the narrative to give a hint of what is to come." What comes is a macabre obsessive science fiction universe, abandoned to drugs and sexual exploitation.*

Naked Lunch, *the novel which propelled William Burroughs into the literary orbit (he was already a light to many writers, having lived what he was to write about) was first published in Paris by Olympia Press, later published in America, and is currently being translated for a French edition. This book and the two that followed have aroused the sensational critical controversy that only major transitions in art provoke. As critics and writers decide why they loathe or revere Burroughs, he takes another leap further out.*

Bulletin From Rewrite: We had to call in the Nova Police to keep all these jokers out of The Rewrite Room—Can't be expected to work under such conditions—Introducing Inspector J. Lee of the Nova Police —"I doubt if any of you on this copy planet have ever seen a Nova criminal—(they take considerable pains to mask their operations) and I am sure none of you have ever seen a Nova police officer—When disorder on any planet reaches a certain point the regulating instance scans POLICE—Otherwise—Sput— Another planet bites the cosmic dust—I will now explain something of the mechanisms and techniques of Nova which are always deliberately manipulated—I am quite well aware that no one on any planet likes to see a police officer so let me emphasize in passing that the Nova police have no intention of remaining after their work is done—That is, when the danger of Nova is removed from this planet we will move on to other assignments—We do our work and go—

"The basic Nova technique is very simple: Always create as many insoluble conflicts as possible and always aggravate existing conflicts—This is done by dumping on the same planet life forms with incompatible conditions of existence—There is of course nothing 'wrong' about any given life form since 'wrong' only has reference to conflicts with other life forms—The point is these life forms should not be on the same planet—Their conditions of life are basically incompatible in present time form and it is precisely the work of the Nova Mob to see that they remain in present time form, to create and aggravate the conflicts that lead to the explosion of a planet, that is to Nova —At any given time recorders fix the nature of obsolute need and dictate the use of total weapons—Like this: take two opposed pressure groups— Record the most violent and threatening statements of group one with regard to group two and play back to group two—Record the answer and take it back to group one— Back and forth between opposed pressure groups—This process is known as "feed-back"—You can see it operating in any bar room quarrel—In any quarrel for that matter—Manipulated on a global scale it feeds back nuclear war and Nova—These conflicts are deliberately created and aggravated by Nova criminals—The Nova Mob: 'Sammy the Butcher,' 'Green Tony,' 'The Brown Artist,' 'Jacky Blue Note,' 'Limestone John,' 'Izzy the Push,' 'Hamburger Mary,' 'Paddy The Sting,' 'The Subliminal Kid,' 'The Blue Dinosaur,' 'Willy the Rat' (who informed on his associates) and 'Mr. & Mrs. D' also known as 'Mr. Bradly', 'Mr. Martin' also known as 'The Ugly Spirit,' thought to be the leader of the mob —The Nova Mob—In all my experience as a police officer I have never seen total fear and degradation on any planet—We intend to arrest these criminals and turn them over to the Biological Department for the indicated alterations—

"Now you may well ask whether we can straighten out this mess to the satisfaction of any life forms involved and my answer is this— Your earth case must be processed by the Biological Courts—(admittedly in a deplorable condition at this time)—No sooner set up than immediately corrupted so that they convene every day in a different location like floating dice games, constantly swept away by stampeding forms all idiotically glorifying their stupid ways of life—(Most of them quite unworkable of course)—attempting to seduce the judges into Venusian sex practices, drug the court officials, and intimidate the entire audience chamber with the threat of Nova—In all my experience as a police officer I have never seen such total fear of the indicated alterations on any planet—A thankless job you see and we only do it so it won't have to be done some place else under even more difficult circumstances—

"The success of the Nova Mob depended on a blockade of the planet that allowed them to operate with impunity—This blockade was broken by partisan activity directed from the planet Saturn that cut the control lines of word and image laid down by the Nova Mob—So we moved in our agents and started to work keeping always in close touch with partisans—The selection of local personnel posed a most difficult problem—Frankly we found that most existing police agencies were hopelessly corrupt—The Nova Mob had seen to that—Paradoxically some of our best agents were recruited from the ranks of those who are called criminals on this planet—In many instances we had to use agents inexperienced in police work—There were of course casualties and fuck-ups—You must understand that an undercover agent witnesses the most execrable cruelties while he waits helpless to intervene, sometimes for many years, before he can make a definitive arrest—So it is no wonder that green officers occasionally slip control when they finally do move in for the arrest—This condition, known as 'arrest fever,' can upset an entire operation—In one recent case, our man in Tangiers suffered an attack of 'arrest fever' and detained everyone on his view screen including some of our undercover men—He was transferred to paper work in another area—Let me explain *how* we make an arrest—Nova criminals are not three-dimensional organisms —(though they are quite definite organisms as we shall see)—but they need three-dimensional human agents to operate—The point at which the criminal controller intersects a three-dimensional human agent is known as 'a coordinate point'—And if there is one thing that carries over from one human host to another and established identity of the controller it is *habit:* idiosyncracies, vices, food preferences—(we were able to trace Hamburger Mary through her fondness for peanut butter)—a gesture, a special look, that is to say the *style* of the controller—A chain smoker will always operate through chain smokers, an addict through addicts —Now a single controller can operate through thousands of human agents, but he must have a line of coordinate points—Some move on junk lines through addicts of the earth, others move on lines of certain sexual practices and so forth— It is only when we can block the controller out of all coordinate points available to him and flush him out from host cover that we can make a definitive arrest— Otherwise the criminal escapes to other coordinate"—

Question: "Inspector Lee, I don't quite understand what is meant by a 'coordinate point'—Could you make that point a little clearer?—

Answer: "Certainly—You see these criminal controllers occupy human bodies—Ghosts? Phantoms? Not at all—Very definite organisms indeed—True you can't see them— Can you see a virus?—Well, the criminal controllers operate in very much the same manner as a virus— Now a virus in order to invade, damage and occupy the human organism must have a gimmick to get in—Once in, the virus invades, damages and occupies a certain area or organ in the body—Known as the tissue of predilection—Hepatitis,

for example, attacks the liver—Influenza, the respiratory tract—Polio and rabies, the central nervous system—In the same way a controller invades damages and occupies some pattern or configuration of the human organism"—

Question: "How do these controllers gain access to the human organism?"

Answer: "I will give an example: the controllers who operate through addiction to opiates—That is who occupy and control addicts of the earth—Their point of entry is of course the drug itself—And they maintain this coordinate point through addiction"—

Question: "What determines the choice of coordinate point? Why does one controller operate through addiction in preference to other channels?"—

Answer: "He operates through addicts because he himself is an addict—A heavy metal addict from Uranus—What we call opium or junk is a very much diluted form of heavy metal addiction—Venusians usually operate through sexual practices—In short, these controllers brought their vices and diseases from their planet of origin and infected the human hosts very much in the same way that the early colonizers infected so-called primitive populations"—

Question: "Inspector Lee, how can one be sure that someone purporting to be a Nova police officer is not an imposter?"—

Answer: "It is not always easy, especially during this transitional period. There are imposters, 'shake men,' who haunt atomic installations and victimize atomic scientists in much the same way as spurious police officers extort money from sexual deviants in public lavatories —In one recent case a well-organized shake mob, purporting to represent the Nova Police, confiscated cyclotrons and other atomic equipment which they subsequently sold on the Uranian black market to support their heavy metal habits— They were arrested and sent away for the thousand year cure—Since then we have encountered a few sporadic cases—Cranks, lunatics for the most part"—

Question: "Inspector Lee, do you think that the Nova Mob can be defeated? —

Answer: "Yes—Their control machine has been disconnected by partisan activity"—

"Now we can move in for some definitive arrests—

" 'Sammy The Butcher' dissolved his dummy cover—His burning metal eyes stabbed at the officer from the molten core of a hot blue planet—The officer moved back dissolving all connections with The Blue Planet, connections formed by the parasite dummy which had entered his body at birth, carefully prepared moulds and association locks closed on empty space— Sammy's eyes burned and sputtered incandescent blue and went out in a smell of metal—His last white-hot blast exploded in empty space—The officer picked up the microphone: 'Sammy The Butcher,' arrested—'Paddy The Sting,' arrested—'Hamburger Mary' has defected—'Green Tony' has surrendered—move in for the definitive arrest of 'Mr. Bradly, Mr. Martin' also known as 'Mr. and Mrs. D' also known as 'The Ugly Spirit'—

'Sammy The Butcher' dissolved his ranks of self-righteous millions and stabbed at the officer dripping Marilyn Monroe Planet—Locks closed on empty space lettering 'My Fair Lady'—In three-dimensional terms 'The Ugly Spirit' and 'Mrs. D' screamed through female blighted continent—So we turn over The Board Books and all the ugliness I had forgotten—Criminal Street— Punitive legislation screaming for more association locks in electric chair and gas chamber—Technical death overt the land—White no-smell of death dripping nova—'The Ugly Spirit' was flushed out of one host cover after the other—Blanked out by our static and silence waves— Call The Old Doctor twice 'Mr. and Mrs. D'—He quiets you remember? —Finished—No shelter—A handful of dust—Screaming clawing for the Nova switch 'The Ugly Spirit' was dragged from the planet—From all the pictures and words of ugliness that have been his place of residence since he moved in on The New World—The officer with silent inflexible authority closed one coordinate point after another—Only this to say: 'Would you rather talk to the partisans "Mr. and Mrs. D"? —Well?—No terms—This is definitive arrest—'Sammy The Butcher' has been taken—There are no guards capable to protect you— Millions of voices in your dogs won't do you a bit of good—Voices fading—Crumpled cloth bodies? —Your name fading across newspapers of the earth—Madison Avenue machine is disconnected— Errand boy closing their errand boys—Won't be much left—Definitive arrest of The Boards as you listen, as the officer closes track— Self-righteous ugliness of their space programme a joke—Written in symbols blighted America: $ $ $— American scent of memory pictures —The idiot honky-tonks of Panhandle Humiliation Outhouse and snarling ugliness of dying peoples— Bourbon soaked legislators from 'marijuana is deadlier than cocaine' —Board Book symbol chains lynch mobs—The White Smoke of pressure group relying on rectum suburbs and the no smell of death—Control Avenue and Hollywood, look at the bread line—The Ugly Spirit retreated back to the '20s in servants and police and the dogs of H.J. Anschlinger—Into one battered host after another—Blanked out board instructions—Silence—Silence—Silence— Call the old money equipment information files of memory—Finished —No shelter—A hand falls across newspapers of the earth for the Nova Switch—Won't do you a bit of good, collaborators with ugliness and degraded flesh—Traitors to all souls everywhere moved in on The New World—The Old Doctor cleaving a heavy silent authority closed one coordinate point after another— The Board is near right now—This to say: Would you rather talk up relying on money?—Fading voice terms?—This is definitive arrest through dying air—There are no guards now capable guide humiliations—Poisonous cloud, millions of dogs won't do you a bit of good— Parasites, crumpled cloth bodies— Your control books fading cross newspaper of the earth couldn't form Nova—Operation completed —Planet out of danger—Proceed with the indicated alterations"—

Train wreck

Conductor:
"O Humankind! Zendicmind!
Centaur O Manticore! Beests!
Panda! I am no better than the . . .
Okapi! Gorilla, I am not more
godly than you . . .
Gnu! If the vulture is low . . . O
Worm! then I am low; somethings
I have done the wildest animal
could not do . . . O God! I took a
swipe at birds . . . told people
birds were spies; cats are spies too;
dogs I saw as monsters; I was
MAN! A million times greater
than ZOO . . . O Kola O Goose I
am no better than you—"

Professor:
"Samothrace! Coat rack! Paintings
with real eyes! Indians dying on
horseback on automobile streets!
Horned turtle at the foot of the
bed! Five-finger'd ants! Bicycles to
run people down! Lost dimes!
Eannatum believes he is wise yet
realizes wise men believe otherwise;
every cuneiform he ever set to
shard was the dire result of some
misery . . . News! Buses! Subway
escape! 87 killed in train wreck . . .
The bus or the street screams
abusive halts; two boys are fist-
fighting; an old lady drunk falls
gash blood splash . . . Down the
subway! No more noises, only
train noises . . . train stops at
train wreck."

Physicist:
"O terminals and sooty shades!
The wrinkled angel weeps
axlegrease . . . Steaming-blue
pop-popping bolts! Deathicity's
mega-voltage increase! Thermo-
tankage freeze! Spinning steel
wheels! Acetylene blue cannot undo
the mangled criers . . . Lancastrian
roses assailed by track; loco-sorcery
toots through damned stations,
deceptive light: in the distance the
little light becomes a train, again
and again; Black Death Stop, the
conductor-dowser leans on the
lever, lovers in multiple-crash."

Man looking for his hand:
"Nightmare's eyeless nightingale
walks soaked in gasoline,
splattering black dung on the
platform . . . Nightmare's crazy
Russian stokes the tank's furnace;
in another nightmare he put a
kopeck on the track; children
waited with excitement; the little
light became a train and went, and
the kopeck was flat and shiny new;
he enticed the children to lay down
their kopecks too, they happily
scattered among the tracks, they

believed in him, they were no
longer afraid of the tracks . . .
Screeching flashes! Little lights
were trains TRAINS! *Oh god oh
god.* The crazy man turns into a
nightingale with sharp teeth;
laughing . . . flies away—"

A walking fish with the face of the
man who taught Blake everything
holds a long rod and taps the
track for irregularities; he turns
the red signal green and stands
flat against the tunnelside; the
distant light becomes a train;
clacking windows aglow, old faces
young faces male faces female faces
clickclack, gone; he turns green
back to red and continues to
search the track for irregularities—

Poet:
"Hence, wreathed derailment,
Casey Jones's laughing skull, the
last puff of steam, the last wheel
spun, the last scream removed,
coffee taste like steel in the
rescuer's mouth; the silver night
eye could not face it; throughout
the night it summoned many a
black cloud to erase it—

"Nightgirls in blackest leather . . .
O loadsome stretches of future!
Black polar cow at bay—Circle
troops of Fate, earth-shaped
Destiny, direct-death straight

arrow, semi-circle crow, carrion-
edged ring, spiral mortification,
gas-rings glued on gas-rings trim
and narrow gas-tube . . . Sedentary
diadem— Inself-hydra, infant
many mouthed, and only one teat;
no wonder the spirit-beest defines
its own—"

Body fished from the Seine

He floats down the Seine
The last victim of the FLN
He's Arab, he's soft, he's green
"He's a long time in the water
    been"
They're dragging him up now
Rope around his waist against the
    prow
Like a wet sponge he bounces and
    squirts
Somehow you feel though dead it
    hurts

I turned to Allen & Peter—what
    amazed them
Was not so much the sad victim
But how a big glass-top tourist boat
Stopped and had the tourists take
    note
They fresh from Eiffel and
    Notre-Dame
—A break of camera calm

147

A French boy's Sunday

Clean are our Sunday clothes,
we must take care not to dirty
    them!
Today's church day a rainy day O
    what a bad day!
Angel, with your chomping on
    white apples,
your wings are dipping in the
    muddy rain
O don't shake them, don't splatter
    our clothes
else our mother pull our ears!

Oh the Paris pissoirs on a cold
    rainy Sunday!
How lonely and damp and hard,
no love in the pissoirs!
And the grey pigeons all wet and
    hunched,
steamy iron and street-stone
    oppression,
careless ledges and pediments under
    which birds soak,
and splash their milky dung on the
    churchyard green,
the soggy dungy nobody-gives-a-
goddam green!

Look at those old ones whispering
    hates
between their prayers and
    medicines;
that's what it's like every Sunday,
no love! no hope! then awful
    back-to-school Monday!

148

What is there to pray about
    outside, for all their tears, the
    poor pissoirs
must contend with our wines,
    Pschitt, and fears.

WHITMAN'S MANY LOVES
by WALTER LOWENFELS

"Publish my name as that of the tenderest lover," Walt Whitman wrote; he might have added "and the most potent one." He loved literally hundreds of young men, and they responded. I know this because I recently examined the letters he had received from soldiers he visited in Washington hospitals during the Civil War. (1) They are intimate letters of love that Whitman kept all his life.

"I can't find words to tell you the love thier (sic) is in me for you," one young soldier writes. "You seemed like a father' . . . 'but such has been the case with thousands of fellow soldiers," another says. And a mother tells him, in similar vein, "You have been more than a brother to James . . . and I still ask you to be a Father and Mother to him." Ten years after the war, a veteran wrote: "We have had a son borned since we heard from you. We call him Walter Whitman in honor to you, for love of you."

Although these letters supply illuminating evidence on the relations between Whitman and his "soldier-boys," I have scanned thousands of words about Whitman's sex life, without finding the correspondence quoted.

One soldier frequently referred to as arousing Whitman's "perturbations"*is Tom Sawyer. In a letter to him, Whitman tells how he said goodbye to their friend Lewey Browne: "When I came away he reached up his face, I put my arm around him and we gave each other a long kiss, half a minute long . . ."

Yes, soldiers kissed him and he kissed them, and they loved each other. There was nothing furtive about it. "He loves everything and everybody," John Burroughs reported. "I saw a soldier the other day stop on the street and kiss him." (2)

In one of the many letters Whitman sent out asking for donations to help buy gifts and goodies for the wounded soldiers he was visiting and consoling, he wrote: "I pet them, some of them it does so much good, they are so faint and lonesome—at parting at night I sometimes kiss them right and left. The doctors tell me I supply the patients with a medicine all their drugs and bottles and powders are helpless to yield." (3)

To his friend Abby Price, Whitman wrote: "How one gets to love them! There is little petting in the

*Whitman's own word.

149

soldier's life in the field, but, Abby, I know what is in their hearts . . . What mutual attachments and how passing deep and tender these boys . . . love for them lives as long as I draw breath . . . These soldiers know how to love, too, when they have the right person and the right love offered them . . ."

In all the vast correspondence and notebooks that have survived, the only evidence of consummated homosexuality is in his poems. In referring to them, he once wrote: "Doubtless I could not have perceived the universe or written one of the poems, if I had not freely given myself to comrades and to love." (4)

Indeed, Whitman's great postwar attachment to the young Washington streetcar conductor, Peter Doyle, raises the question whether such affairs were physically consummated —at any rate, after he had passed his 30's. (His letters to Doyle have been published.) (5) After Whitman's death Doyle was interviewed; he confirmed the evidence of the correspondence that their devotion to each other was not sexual in the ordinary sense.

In 1890, when Whitman was 71, John Addington Symonds, the English critic who wrote one of the first (and best) books on Whitman, suggested that Whitman was, like himself, "an unrepresentative" man (to use Henry Seidel Canby's phrase). Whitman responded*: "About the question on Calamus, etc., it is only rightly to be construed by and within its own atmosphere and essential character—all its pages and pieces so coming strictly under. That the *Calamus* part has ever allowed the possibility of such construction as mentioned is terrible. I am fain to hope that the pages themselves are not to be even mentioned for such gratuitous and quite at the time undreamed and unwished possibility of morbid inference—which are disavowed by me and seem damnable . . . My life, young manhood, mid-age, times South &c., have been jolly, bodily, and doubtless open to criticism. Though unmarried I have had six children—two are dead, one living Southern grandchild, fine boy, writes to me occasionally—circumstances (connected with their fortune and benefit) have separated me from intimate relations." (6)

Scholars have agreed that these were dream children. like the others to whom he referred in a letter to

*A personal friend of Whitman's, Thomas Donaldson, makes it clear (in *Walt Whitman, the Man;* Harpers, N.Y. 1896) that he thought Whitman put into his poems "the passionate love of comrades" . . . "not out of his experience but out of his loneliness."

his friend and disciple, Dr. Bucke, a year before his death: "I have two deceased children (young man & woman: illegitimate, of course) that I much desired to bury here with me—but have ab't abandoned the plan on account of angry litigation and fuss generally, and disinterment from down South." (7)

In his letters, Whitman didn't hesitate, late in his life, to refer to youthful love affairs that all scholars agree were non-existent. He did not, however, mention to his literary correspondents, nor to anyone else, the "Frenchy" we shall meet later, nor the mysterious Miss (or Mrs.) "164," with whom, as we shall see, he seems to have had a desperate affair in Washington, 1868-1870 (when Whitman was 50 and past his prime as poet). Nor does he refer anywhere—in poems, letters or notebooks—to the "lady of the tintype" I found in one of his earlier notebooks—dated 1859, when he was 40, and living in New York.

One fact is certain: Whitman consistently refused to eliminate one comma from his love poems, even though he was under considerable pressure to do so. (8) He has described a two-hour walk up and down the Boston Common in 1860 with Emerson, who wanted him to make some deletions in the third edition of *Leaves of Grass*, then at the printer's: "During these two hours he was the talker and I the listener. It was an argument—statement, reconnoitering, review, attack, and pressing home (like an army corps in order, artillery, cavalry, infantry) of all that could be said against that part (and a main part) in the construction of my poems *Children of Adam* . . . 'What have you to say to such things?' said E, pausing in conclusion. 'Only that while I can't answer them at all, I feel more settled than ever to adhere to my own theory, and exemplify it' . . . " (9)

"Without shame," Whitman wrote in *A Woman Waits for Me*, "the man I like knows and avows the deliciousness of his sex/Without shame the woman I like knows and avows hers."

Was there such a woman in his life? Nobody knows, although in actuality there is probably more evidence (outside the poems) of sexual relations with women than there is about specific homosexuality. A vast body of material in letters, notes, journals, reveals his attachments to hundreds of men—including firemen, mechanics, New York bus drivers—in addition to the soldiers in Washington (10), but all we know about them is the kisses and hugs so often mentioned. Beyond this, we don't know what was implied when Whitman records in a notebook: "Friday night, October 11, 1862 . . . met a 19-year-old blacksmith David Wilson walking up Middaugh Street—slept with me . . ." (11) We do know that Whitman's kisses were not limited to young workers or soldiers. "He kissed me as if I were a girl," Whitman's friend John Burroughs observed.

On the other hand, in a notebook dated 1868, (12) we do meet the unnamed "her" whom he identifies only by the number "16" or "164":

"Cheating, childish abandonment of myself, fancying what does not really exist in another, but is all the time in myself alone—utterly deluded & cheated by *myself* & my own weakness O REMEMBER WHERE I AM MOST WEAK & most lacking. Yet always preserve a kind spirit & demeanour to 16. But PURSUE HER NO MORE . . ."

"June 17. *It is* IMPERATIVE, that I obviate & remove myself (& my orbit) *at all hazards* [away from] this *in cessant* [*enormous*] & enormous PERTURBATION . . ."

And in 1870:

"June 15. To GIVE UP ABSOLUTELY & *for good, from this present hour,* [all] this FEVERISH FLUCTUATING, useless undignified pursuit of 164 . . ." (13)

I agree with Whitman scholars that "16" and "164" were probably the same person. Was she in any sense related to the Washington names and addresses he kept in his notebooks which some scholars believe were "*petites maisons?*"*

Did Whitman carry over into his life what he said in his poem "To A Common Prostitute," " . . . be at ease with me—/ Not till the sun excludes you do I exclude you"?

There is one mysterious unknown who makes a shadowy appearance in Whitman's life as a "frenchy." I came across a reference to her in a letter I found in the vast manuscript collection of Charles Feinberg, in Detroit, while I was engaged in research for WALT WHITMAN'S CIVIL WAR. The letter is from Will H. Wallace, a surgeon Whitman probably knew from his earlier bohemian days in New York and apparently met again in the Washington hospitals. Wallace left Washington to work in General Hospital No. 3, in Nashville. From there he

---

*On the front flyleaf of one of Whitman's Civil War notebooks (now in the Library of Congress), we find: "Mad'lle Sophie Favarger, 257—E. Sutter, cor E & 11th St.," and the last entry in a notebook where he kept his diary reads: "Mad'selle Navazias, 260 Penn av 3d floor . . ."

wrote Whitman, April 3, 1863:

"I have five young ladies who act in the capacity of nurses—i.e., *one of them* is French (14), young and beautiful to set your eyes upon. Can you not visit us and note for yourself?"

Whitman's reply has not been found, but the following month Wallace wrote him again: "I am surprised at your frenchy leaving you in such a deplorable state, but you are not alone. I had to dismiss mine, to save the reputation of the hospital and your humble servant . . ."

Was there a "Frenchy" or "Frenchies"? In his closing years, Whitman claimed in conversation with his young friend Traubel, who was recording every word: "I used to get love letters galore, those days, perfumed letters—from girls down there," and when he showed Traubel a trifling gift that was made for him, he said, "By a clerk in Washington, a girl who was sweet to me."

Whitman's notebook of 1859, in the Library of Congress, has a tintype of a young woman pasted in it. She is described by Canby as "rather carelessly dressed, sensuous mouth and eyes, heavy ringlets, revealing on one side of her face what seems to be an eardrop, graceful hands and wrists of which she seems to be proud. Her clothes are heavy but not unfashionable—a plaid waist under a coat with flowing sleeves, tied at the breast by a corded collar, with a pleated, heavy skirt, apparently a brunette. I record my opinion—for what it may be worth—that this obviously intellectual, probably 'unrefined,' evidently sensuous and presumably passionate girl from the undifferentiated people is the kind of woman and probably the only kind of woman, with whom the complex Whitman could have had rewarding physical experiences—whether for the night or a year . . ."

Canby adds, "Whatever may be said of the *Calamus* items" (about love between men), "the poems of *Children of Adam* are the sublimation of the passion of real love . . . not all sublimated."

Aside from the poems celebrating Whitman's love and respect for women, the testimony that distinguished women have contributed is very eloquent. A contemporary critic (Mary A. Chilton, of Islip, Long Island) wrote in the *Saturday Press*, June 9, 1860: "I see him now as the apostle of purity (who) vindicates manhood and womanhood from the charges of infamy, degradation and vice." And in the same magazine another woman writes (June 23), "Walt ennobles everything he writes about."

Mrs. Ellen O'Connor,* a close friend, at whose house Whitman lived for a time and afterwards visited frequently, wrote in *The Atlantic Monthly* (June, 1907), that Whitman "with his strong lungs and loud voice" denounced "free love" as "damnable."

Another gifted woman, Mrs Anne Gilchrist, an English literary critic who wrote a powerful estimate of Whitman's work—the first serious essay on him by a woman—fell in love with the poet across the Atlantic Ocean, after reading *Leaves of Grass*. Mother of two grown children and a widow, Mrs. Gilchrist took Whitman's poems as a personal message addressed to her. After an exchange of letters, in which he urged her *not* to come, she nevertheless left England for the United States, to be his "mate."

Their relationship may shed some light on Whitman's ambivalence. Mrs. Gilchrist settled in Philadelphia with her son and daughter, to be near Whitman. They became close friends—who never kissed. She found that the Whitman of the love poems and the Whitman who took the ferry from his Camden home to visit her were apparently unrelated.

*William O'Connor, author of "The Good Gray Poet," was one of Whitman's best friends.

If this lady, whose great love for Whitman drew her across the ocean, couldn't in Whitman's own presence penetrate his contradictions, how can we arrive at the final word, a century later, dealing not with a flesh-and-blood man, but with scraps of paper-letters, notes, poems?

In the course of his conversations with Traubel, Whitman hinted several times that he would one day tell him his Great Secret. If this concerned his love life, there is no record of his ever having divulged it; it remains shrouded in the ambiguity we seem to find everywhere.

What emerges appears to be a man who, like many other writers, lived one life in his books and another outside them. Whitman himself once told a visitor (Edward Carpenter): "I think there are truths which it is necessary to envelop or wrap up . . . there is something in my nature, furtive like an old hen."

We seem to arrive at more questions rather than final answers. From the prose evidence, it would appear that Whitman probably had sexual relations with women—possibly as late as his 50's. The direct evidence of sexual involvement with men is confined to poems written during his 30's. Why then the general impression that Whitman was exclusively homosexual?

The reasons may be summarized:

(1) He did love hundreds of young men; he had particular attachments to several of them. This violates the normal cultural pattern, which concentrates on sex acts between men and women.

(2) Whitman never married* and had no major love relationship with a woman. The references I have unearthed about his affairs with two or three unnamed women I found in obscure sources, known only in scattered bits to a few Whitmaniacs and brought together for the first time in this essay.

(3) Ever since his first book* was published over a century ago and up to our own day, Whitman has been attacked by some for writing immorally about sex—particularly about love between men. That has spread his reputation—as regards his sexuality—far beyond the circle of his readers. His contemporary, Whittier, is supposed to have thrown *Leaves* into the fire; only recently there was considerable protest when the new Camden-Philadelphia bridge was named in honour of the poet who used to cross the Delaware by ferry.

(4) The kind of young men to whom he was drawn were not his intellectual peers, but "of the roughs." This falls into a pattern with which we are familiar from the lives of other intellectuals who had homosexual experiences (Hart Crane is a recent example).

(5) The main reason for Whitman's reputation as a homosexual lies in his poems. In them he not only described intimate physical contacts— he announced himself a prophet of a new religion of love between men. This was to be the basis for fulfilling American democratic ideas . . . "ideals of manly love . . . I will lift what has too long kept down these smoldering fires/ I will give them complete abandonment/ I will write the evangel-poems of comrades and of love."

The central question remains: How does the evidence of love in his poems relate to his personal experiences?

It is, I believe, unrealistic to try to find precise factual documentation about Whitman's love life in his poems, just as it would be to try to indentify from them the carpenter who made the mechanism Whitman sang about in "Out of the Cradle Endlessly Rocking."

Whitman's use of sexual love and imagery was deliberate and programmatic, rather than confessional and autobiographic. That, of course,

*Mrs. O'Connor remembered that in his Washington days, "Whitman upheld the modern theory of marriage being the true and ideal relation between the sexes."

156

is why he refused to censor it, even on his death bed.* It stood for a central theme in his work that he would not and could not allow to be eliminated; it was part of a prophetic programme and a vision of a world to be dominated by love, freedom, equality—not only politically but sexually, and not only between but among the sexes.

The essential question isn't what Whitman did in his private life. The only reason that it is of interest is because of what he did in his poems. There he elevated not only men but women, too, to a higher level than they had enjoyed in literature before. Whatever his experiences were, he turned them (at his best) into great verbal celebrations of human beings as individuals and "en masse."

And yet, with all his love of many men and some women, none of them could satisfy his vast desire. There is one confession about this that I believe to be absolutely accurate. It is the passage in which he tells us that his big seminal affair was the universe:

"The known universe has one complete lover, and that is the greatest poet . . . He consumes an eternal passion . . . He is no irreso-

lute or suspicious lover—he is sure—he scorns intervals . . . The sea is not surer of the shore, or the shore of the sea, than he is of the fruition of his love . . ." (15)

NOTES

1 A manuscript collection of soldiers' letters to Whitman is contained in a folder entitled "A Series of 94 soldiers' letters addressed to Walt Whitman, 1863, etc.," in the Berg Collection, N.Y. Public Library.

2 Clara Barrus, *The Life and Letters of John Burroughs,* Boston, 1925.

3 Horace L. Traubel, *With Walt Whitman in Camden,* Boston, 1906; N.Y., 1908.

4 This passage occurs in the 1866 edition of *Calamus* # 39, retitled in 1867 "Sometimes With One I Love," with these lines changed to: "I loved a certain person ardently and my love was not returned. Yes out of that I have written these songs."

5 See *Calamus* (Whitman's Letters to Peter Doyle), edited by R. M. Bucke, (Boston, Laurens Maynard, 1897). Also in *Complete Writings,* G. P. Putnam's Sons, 1902, N.Y. & London.

6 Edward Carpenter, *Days with Walt Whitman* (London, George Allen, 1906).

7 *The Uncollected Poetry and Prose of Walt Whitman,* Emory Holloway, N.Y. Doubleday Page and Co., 1921.

8 He did consent to the publication in 1868 in England of "Selections" edited by Dante Gabriel Rossetti, who omitted poems he thought would not pass the censor or might offend the "squeamishness" of the times.

9 *Specimen Days,* Complete Prose by Walt Whitman, D. Appleton & Co., N.Y., 1909.

*"In the long run the world will do as it pleased with the book. I am determined to have the world know what I was pleased to do." (16)

10 Many of his young N.Y. friends are identified in "Walt Whitman's Middle Years," an unpublished doctoral thesis by George L. Sixbey, 1940 (Yale University Library).

11 In a notebook in the Library of Congress.

12 In the Library of Congress.

13 There seems to have been an initial originally, which was erased and the number "16" written in. The number "164" is written in over a dash.

14 Emphasis in the original. Both Wallace letters are in the Feinberg Collection, Detroit.

15 *Preface to the* 1855 *Edition,* Complete Prose, Op. Cit.

16 *An Executor's Diary Note,* 1891, Leaves of Grass, edited by Emory Holloway, Garden City, 1957.

THE SPY'S CORNER
by TERRY SOUTHERN

"NEW ART MUSEUM IN HAMBURG BLOWN UP"

Hamburg, W. Germany, Dec. 13 (Reuters). While an estimated 150 persons waited outside in the pouring rain, for the opening of the swank new Das Rheingeld museum in the Lebenhausen section, a series of explosions were heard inside the museum. As the crowd dispersed in panic, a much larger explosion occurred, collapsing the entire building. As far as could be determined, no injuries were sustained by the crowd—some of whom returned to the site and picked about in the rubble, turning up bits of plaster and fragments of oil-stained canvas, though nothing large enough to reveal the nature or merit of the paintings themselves. Several persons reported that the small pieces of canvas mysteriously "disappeared" after a short time.

Preliminary investigation failed to determine the precise cause of the explosions, although what appeared to be wired detonation devices were found throughout the debris. Museum officials could not be reached for comment, nor, in fact, could their exact identity be immediately determined, though it is

158

presumed that they are in some way connected with the new school of painting in the Lebenhausen, the so-called "neo-Nada" group, whose work was to be exhibited publicly yesterday at the museum opening, after months of intensive advertising. Gallery owners in various parts of the city, as well as artists of other schools, were cautious in their comments as to the merit of the neo-Nada painting, which had never been shown before. "We must wait and see," was the general attitude.

On a recent visit to Hamburg we had opportunity to speak with 32 year-old Ernest Badhoff, one of the leading exponents of the new school, shortly following their ill-fated *vernissage* at the Rheingeld museum. The interview took place in English, and was recorded on tape. A verbatim transcript of the conversation follows:

Q: I find it curious that Hamburg should be experiencing this resurgence of advanced creativity.

Herr Badhoff: Nothing could be more logical. Germany is a nation of philosophers and *art,* after all, is merely an extension of philosophy—a clever or attractive way of making a philosophic statement. My God, what a sense of *realism* it has brought! A strange new kind of realism—an almost *imaginative* real-ism, you might say.

Q: I see. Well, now about your work—the work of the neo-Nada group—how many are you?

Herr Badhoff: I am not at liberty to divulge that. I can tell you this much, our vernissage featured the work of twelve painters.

Q: You mean the October 1st show at the Rheingeld?

Herr Badhoff: Yes. I had seven paintings in the show, the others about the same. In all, there were 85 paintings in the show.

Q: Well, perhaps I'm mistaken, but I was given to understand that your work—the work of your group—has not yet been shown publicly nor, in fact, has it been seen by anyone I've been able to meet.

Herr Badhoff: You see, ideally a painting—or any other work of art, for that matter—occurs, both in conception and execution, solely in the mind of the artist. Only persons unsure of their conceptions, and lacking any inner sense of form and colour, find it necessary to bring the painting into material existence. Such persons, of course, have no real or noteworthy connection with contemporary art.

Q: I see. Well, now I understand there is an *American* here who is quite prominent in your group.

Herr Badhoff: That is correct. Jack Dandy he is called—he was here during the war, as a soldier, and deserted from the U.S. Army. As you may know, he is a quadruple amputee, one of very few.

Q: I see. Well, how does he manage to paint with this . . . this very serious handicap?

Herr Badhoff: All I can say is he literally throws himself into his canvas.

Q: But you have never actually *seen* his work, have you?

Herr Badhoff: Again correct. No one has seen his work. We do not *show* our work, not to anyone.

Q: Now your vernissage at the Rheingeld was spoiled, wasn't it— by the explosions, I mean. How did that happen?

Herr Badhoff: No, no, that *was* the vernissage.

Q: The work, the paintings, deliberately destroyed?

Herr Badhoff: No, no, that isn't the point. You have to see the *totality* of it. The paintings did not exist at the time of the explosions. Those paintings were done with an oil-based pigment, you understand, tinctured with acid—sulphuric acid, six-percent solution—giving them a physical duration of about 72 hours. The paintings were non-existent *before* the explosions.

Q: Well, now just what was the point?

Herr Badhoff: The point? What point?

Q: Well, of the whole thing.

Herr Badhoff: Ah yes, *that* was the point—the "whole thing!" Yes, that was the point precisely!

Q: But at the time you were hanging your pictures for the show, you must have seen some of the other work then.

Herr Badhoff: Ah ha! No, I did not! We did not see each others' work at that time. Each canvas was covered with a loose drape which had been treated with a seventy-percent acid solution. This drape dissolved in about two hours —by which time we were all out of the building. But—and this might interest you—for perhaps six hours, there were 85 marvellous, never before seen, pictures there on exhibition, in a totally empty museum!

Q: And then . . .

Herr Badhoff: Ka-blooie! Nada!

Q: It is difficult to understand how *patronage* can occur if there are no paintings to be seen or purchased.

Herr Badhoff: Well, you must realize that as an art evolves, so does its patronage. Patrons come to expect quite different things from what they expected in the past.

Q: And just what do you give your patrons in exchange for their support?

Herr Badhoff: What any art gives

its patrons—the privilege of identifying with the latest and greatest.

Q: May I ask if there were any dissentions, for example, to the plan of destroying the museum?

Herr Badhoff: Yes, Jack Dandy wanted the museum filled with people, taking their last earthly look . . . at non-existent paintings! Then ka-blooie! Nada!

Q: Well, that's quite an idea—. Still, I hope *I* never get into one of your showings by mistake, ha, ha.

SICILY ENOUGH
by CLAIRE RABE

Illustrations by
Dennis Bailey

Taormina is an island on a mountain. A female, rising and falling town, I sucked away at it for over a year because I wanted everything.

Dogshadow thin I arrive, carrying my third child like a weapon through this old town, while the only thing I feel is my hair tight, hurting where the baby holds on. A fierce clock, she reminds my vague shocked self that I must function. We kiss and I inhale her breath like food, warm as the milk I flowed into her some months ago.

October in Sicily, and there is the first volcano I have ever seen. Cool mountain, lambent with snow on its mouth; how can it be so hot inside?

I buy grapes, wash them in the fountain while broody dark men watch me bending over. I suddenly feel well-fleshed, and the skin of grapes slides agreeably over my tongue. The baby has fun spitting with them. I buy a great deal more to bring to the other children waiting at home.

It will be easy to eat in this country.

Long walks, up and down steps, going from view to view, the town spread around in broken architecture, painted in tired colour that was once red. Walls better than current art, moonpitted, incredibly dry. What a sun has made all this happen! Centuries of summer, centuries of cats and dogs breeding under Roman arches.

Women who still wear black, faces yellow, a smear of bad flesh under the eyes that arouses me and suggests a hundred perversities. Every woman has breasts and thighs and hair in her armpits; I see them as black curling flowers. Their legs are strong and hairy, men do not force them to shave; here they do not alter animals or their passions.

This directness, this use of the body attracts me at once to the Sicilians and makes me feel warm. There is no subtle sex here, no American sex, but coupling itself. The day for a Sicilian has happened if he has made love. It seems empty to sleep unless it is post-coital; it's lonely.

I long for a lover here as I have longed for dogs to sleep with in my virtuous days. I want warm animals so near me that they are inside.

Desire grows on me. I see it reflected

in the men who stare at me, their lust is an approval of my fattening body. I eat so much now, just to look at the vegetables is to feel nourished. A kind of cauliflower that grows almost nowhere else is in season. The whole top of it is painted deep purple, formidable as the colour runs off into the cooking water till finally eaten, white again, drenched in pungent olive oil.

My children are so well here. They break rough bread and dunk it in sauce, they eat garlic and tomatoes; our cuisine is the maid's who makes lentil soup with pasta, broccoli with rice. We seem to be in a farmer's kitchen. My house is a good smell, while in the garden pomegranates burst on trees and oranges hang like lanterns.

Everything here becomes hazed over by sun and abundance. If something terrible has happened to me I no longer remember it so harshly. I feel as though I have a million senses now, held together by brain and guts. All I have known and suffered and longed for come together for me in Sicily. Good and bad, hard and soft, there is everything in those four words, any combination of them means something. Good soft bad hard or good hard bad soft or. If I am to go on living, and I must, since I have six black eyes looking at me, since my children are happy

and do not understand that someone has died, then I shall become part of this landscape. I will grow into these trees, into these hills, and wait and stare and hope for the volcano to erupt.

There he is, small angry-faced man. As he stands up to greet me a ray of sun slanting through the window grabs his eyes. They glare at me in the agate yellow of certain birds, the pupils pinned on me. I have seen that yellow in the amber I found on the beaches of the Baltic, where I played as a child. I have seen that yellow in the eyes of Clarita when she lusted for me. She was rapacious, like the watching bird, her eyes cold yellow pointed exactly to the centre of me. As his are now.

"You are American?"

"You speak English."

"Not very well."

"Oh, too well. I want to learn Italian."

"You will have a Sicilian accent if you learn from me."

"I want to."

This will be my first lover. I must prepare myself as for the first time ever.

My hair needs to be cut, no more pins in it. I examine my fine skin and bathe it carefully. I polish my children as one does beautiful apples. My walks have a direction now. I go to his bar where he stands in the doorway waiting, sure of me. I had no idea that he is the richest young man in town, the most beautiful. It is his eyes I look for.

We work slowly, he is patient, always teaching, so aware that I am getting ready for him.

We go for many drives, I admire the countryside, and he takes me as far as the snow of the mountain.

How magical the preparation for love.

In the cafe I meet his Sicilian friends. There, every woman who passes is judged. When they approve, "buona" is uttered with a hoarse gusto, and I picture at once an entwining of genitals like the display of entrails in a butcher shop.

The face of the woman is looked at last. She must simply not be ugly. A robust body with abundant breast and rear and a fattish face is a fine "cavallo" or "vaca." The inspection is continuous, noisy with smacks and hisses, an obvious need to make each opinion public, to share. They tell each other exactly how they feel and how they would treat each case.

I have learned quickly to know what they say if only by their gestures. Beautiful in the way of mutes, hands weave away at the meaning of their talk. Hands measure intensity of meaning, but a small downward motion of the mouth destroys an entire argument.

My mother had this way of destroying me. Her mouth is thin and the slightest doubt is immediately visible in the downward arch of her lips—and there is a real shock in me as I know that she is against me. Her mouth curves at me like a snake, her face changes so much there is no chance for the girl to impress this judge. Everything has been smudged over. Is it then that I begin to lie? Or do I just begin to sneak? Sometimes I try again to tell her what I feel and again she makes this unbearable face. More and more I hide what I feel and soon am such an expert that I even cease to feel.

The seduction of my mother failed. She will not marvel at me. As did Clarita when she caressed my young body with her old appreciation, the yellow glowing in her eyes. My mother made me cold. I slept with a million blankets and no heat came; my body was sealed off in a cold young coffin.

And here is a country without music, books, painting, only certain lusts. Of course I must live here; this is why I came to this quicksand where there is no space for sadness, only quick frantic sucking motion, up, down.

Night. Palm trees staring straight

up, sky soft around stars, clouds moving through the heads of trees. Olive, cypress and palm, their different foliage hard in the black distance, trees so separate from one another that one cannot imagine a forest. Palm, cypress, olive; leaf, shape, size, everything unique, blowing up into the sky all at once, the night dark, glowing with such ornament, waiting for its own end.

In the cemetery night pushes against what was, while the cypress rises and small birds rest.

Sound of mandolins in the tavern, sweet and liquid, played by two ugly men, drifting around Roberto like a habit, he hears none of it, just stares at my thighs. The first music I've been able to listen to in a long time, it does not frighten me into the past.

Red wine, fresh from the slopes of the mountain, cheap and delicious like penny candy, I drink it fast, it seems to improve my Italian. The room, square and low, underlit, with a skinny dog asleep on one of the chairs. The owner dedicates a song to me about the torment of love, smiling at the "nuovia coppia" that has the town talking.

I feel pleasant, involved with everything and everyone there. A ditchdigger I have seen working along the streets, dark and beautiful, now dressed in a marvellous velveteen jacket that shines like a chestnut, nods to me but I do not answer. I resent his trying to make real my flirtation with him. I only like to watch him working, to dream about his strength and simplicity, I really wish he would not confuse his reality with my fantasy. "Don't speak," I think, "don't let me hear your voice, just be there and let me dream about you. I don't want to touch you, I just want the idea of you. That's my man there, that handsome creature lounging by my side, more elegant than you, an off-spring of Greeks and Moors with the body Michelangelo had adored."

Yes, my eyes roam the men with ease for I am safe among them, coupled to Roberto whose loins are making me happen.

"Quanto sei bello," I whisper. He grins but has to answer: "A man is simpatico not beautiful."

"I don't speak Italian well, make mistakes, but don't teach me too much."

"Va bene, va bene," he nods, his eyes iridescent, picking up all the light there is in the room.

The piazza where we meet every morning. He in his kingdom, that bar where he strides about like a small emperor.

"You are my empress now," he

says lovingly, so proud.

"No, just your mistress," I answer in a coy way, new to me. His courtship of me has gotten into my bones. I feel all woman, organ deep as I glisten around him, my breasts full.

Walking down the corso, thighs heavy against my sex on this Sicilian street where I pass several times a day, where nothing changes except the flimsiest detail, where I am on parade. They all know what has happened. La Americana, amanti de Roberto. I have fallen into a certain status, condemned yet full of prestige because my lover is rich. Besides, it's not often that a woman with three children has any vitality left here. The women are jealous of my strong body, the men wonder about me. "She must be very good," I overhear. "Che buona."

There is a ritual as I enter through the arch into the wide incredible piazza, more beautiful than the shell in Sienna. I go to the railing that overlooks the sea, trees falling down the view to the sea, the earth dark and dry green. To the right glares Etna. I look there first, no, I behold it. Nearly a perfect cone; it rises strong at the sky, the snow hard and clean, whiter than a nun's eye.

The piazza, bounded by curving, crumbling churches on two sides, with Roberto's bar in between, hypnotises me. I sit for hours at a table, trying every drink ever brought to Italy, looking endlessly at the pure view of space and sky hanging over the piazza where emptiness is broken only by seven trees and the people strolling. Seven oleander trees that never cease to bloom, white, pink and red flowers.

Five miles along the coast, gigantic over the cold sea, rises the town of Forza D'Agro. Lazy in medieval poverty, it waits to be looked at. Roberto and I are spring coming into those black, sunless streets. Shops are tombs for food showing porkfat, tripe, enormous loaves of bread. Awful old people stare at me, disapprove of my tight trousers and the way I hold Roberto's hand. He is clean among them, so young.

Passing a stable I desire him and pull him quickly into the warm smell of manure.

"Let's make love here," I say, but he laughs and worries. I take off my shoes and push my feet into the texture of dung. I suppose I am going too far, but I feel different here, not vicarious but in the actual sway of history. The age of this town has pulled off a certain veneer.

Roberto looks very uncomfortable and tries to get me out. "Questa pazza!" he exclaims. But I do not feel crazy, I simply feel less civilized and wish he would go along with me in my sudden involvement with the twelfth century.

However, his embarrassment has spoiled my mood and I follow him. He wants to show me the town and its silly monuments. While he gapes at a church I smell bread baking. There is the oven, teeming with fire. A donkey stands patiently by the door, so heavily laden with wild rosemary that it resembles a solid halo. "Look," I say. but he hardly knows what I mean. Certainly the church is lovely and I am tempted to steal from it. How I should like one of those wooden candelabras, golden and flaky where worms have been.

Down below in Naxos, the first town built by the Greeks in Sicily, eating prehistoric octopus, while my eyes drift over the splendid view of my island above.

Worn, fabulous landslide of a view, green as black jagging to that sea where lava still lies exposed as it has lain for centuries.

Not thinking of the view; it has been sown into me. His body planted in me, I feel a tree. How shocking in the mirror, how very secret and deep it looks from the outside, while inside there is a wet intensity even deeper than what the mirror shows, and that's very deep. How cataclysmic to be penetrated, those thighs opening wide to let him in.

From a dusty fig tree I take a bursting fruit. It must be splitting to be good. As I am at my full opening, ripe and glad to have this pleasure made known to me. How many women are allowed this as they plough through years of intimacy that are never catastrophic.

Perhaps I am losing my mind in this fleshbath, perhaps I shall lose everything, even my children. I forget them so often now. I have only this spastic, one-dimensional affair, but oh, it goes deep.

I know I do not live in order to remember; at the end memory will be as nothing. To say I really had it, how might it be if in the dry years I would have to say where was it? I do know that what I experience now is important, the future might only matter if I had lacked this.

With or without regret life ends and it makes no difference to me how it will end, only that it will end. It doesn't matter how things turn out; they change anyway. How can I provide for the future, even my children's! What is perfectly clear is that I adore them now and am in touch with life itself three times a day: eating, sleeping and fornicating —there is no other tenderness.

Fatigue pulls me on the bed. I should sleep and become strong for the rash sun tomorrow. It's always too bright in the morning. The day begins fast with the running sounds of children as they continue the day before. For them sleep has been a simple interruption. "Oh, children, your noise is my reality!"

My heart has gone dim in the huddle with night, spread under him like a stain of red wine on a white cloth. I put on dark glasses to protect me from this sun and the size of the mountain growing whiter each day.

How well we know each other, if knowledge has anything to do with these odd gropings over a foreign bed in a foreign country. The man caresses me in Italian: "You are my bread," he says and eats away at me, mushing my body into this incredible fatigue, his weight on me like stones I have helped put there. What am I doing? What is this strange excess?

When he sleeps everything is over, he is merely beautiful—not someone I care for. Why doesn't he leave? I don't need his shut face lying there, his body so still that he might as well be dead.

His sleeping wakes me and I rush to see my children in their beds, afraid they will look dead as well. Oh no, sleep lies on them lightly, on their round breathing faces life is growing.

My mother's thin face over the lush, soft body, this sense of being her all over again. My face is what I saw in her when she was thirty and I needed her most and was lonely for the generous droop of breast that Roberto loves so and uses as though I were his mother.

All dimensions gone here. Just the way the cocks crow in the night as nowhere else. What disturbs them so? Dark night with roosters screaming, wind pouring from the sky in a dry rain; I do not grow older but deeper.

But the weight of my children is a monkey on my back. Impossible to neglect them with ease. Coming home late, so late, I go into their rooms to stare at those simple yielding bodies. One of them coughs and I feel destroyed.

My passion with Roberto is a labyrinth where I hump along from angle to curve, free for a very short time, the white thread of my children wrapping me into a knot instead of leading me out. I go deeper into the maze, dragging them with me while I long to be childless, thoughtless, immune to all former feeling. Often now I lie so still under him, afraid that one more move will make me swoon, blot me out.

In a dark museum where his body is the only statue, more splendid than David, perfect because it's also warm. How well I understand a torso murder for love of each limb. I hack away at him with appalling want. And he, how he spreads himself for me in his self love. He would exhibit his anus without compunction, aware that every part of him is appropriate. I feel like one of those insane collectors who will do anything to acquire a Michelangelo. I am insane till I lie down alone again, pale from greed, sex-rotten.

I know so well that I should leave here. It's the crazy people who make me sure. That one, all dressed in black, a male widow, shouting to the children behind him. I see my own son, angered I pull him away and force him to be sad. "But I wasn't laughing," he says.

The madman stops in the piazza, stands in the centre, a fountain yelling. Everyone laughs. I myself worry. What's wrong with me? For these people sanity is real and insanity is a spectacle not to be taken seriously; the crazy man is a clown. I am considered a sentimental fool. What's to be done in this red and white country?

Every time I leave my villa, lying slightly above the town, I walk slowly down the steps towards the sound below. A kind of welcoming hell swells towards me from the corso where the entire town is walking hard, talking hard, hungry, agitated.

Listen to the noise, it's the only music of the place. There is a strong and evident rhythm; one can tell the time of day by the amount of it, strongest in the evening about seven, before dinner.

I walk through them, only listening, not enchanted by their mess. I crave monotony, don't want anything more to happen, still haven't understood what has happened.

Winter here is a few weeks of rain, hard wind at night that empties the streets. I walk along the corso feeling free and clean.

In the cafe idle men huddle around the fireplace. Roberto sits with me in a corner, worried about business, constantly interrupting me as I try to read a book. I'm sick of his banal problems, how boring he is out of bed. Should he bring prices down, is it going to be a good carnival so that he'll make up for these bad few weeks? I don't care, watch instead his pretty mouth, the nice way he slumps in the chair. I long for a deaf mute.

My house is soaking from all the rain, clothes don't dry, the maid complains, children irritable from staying in so much.

Three weeks of this, the town looks lonely, unprepared as every

170

year for anything but sun. These Sicilians don't realize that it must rain and be cold sometimes. Their houses poorly equipped, they press around puny charcoal fires, old women hide them under long skirts. Several of them die every year from the fumes.

"Cattivo tempo," is all they say, stacking black umbrellas around the rooms where the rain is really in.

Roberto is worried about me, aware of my boredom.

"You'll feel better when the sun shines. I know this place is dull for you like this."

He takes me with him when he buys lemons for the bar. This interests me because we drive through dreary, sick villages, the heart of this country. Such places, all the poverty spilled in the streets, rags of children everywhere while the mothers sit and sew or pee! Whatever vegetable is in season. That's the diet, a plate of fried greens or tomatoes, on good days a rind of meat. Sad looking people, unprotesting, much too used to this.

In the lemon factory it's warm. There are special heated canteens that turn green lemons yellow in a hurry. Women grade the fruit according to size and colour, wrapping the best ones in little papers that makes the crate look festive.

How they stare at me, anxious to know what country I come from. I have soft, friendly talks with these swift-handed women who work ten hours to earn less than a dollar. One of them cuts a thick-fleshed lemon and teaches me to eat it with salt. Roberto watches with delight, glad I'm not bored, pleased when they refer to me as his wife.

The sound of rain is becoming intolerable; it's washing away the glamour of Sicily. These dull people are wearing me down. Roberto seems puny and always thinking about money. When there are no girls to look at the town idlers have long, stupid talks about the government. The only thing they ever read is some sort of reactionary newspaper that makes more ado about the killings than politics. Amazing, dreary murders happen every day in this last country, always involving hatchets or other farm implements. The Taormina citizens are proud of their clean record. Of course they have the Greek theatre that brings them slews of tourists every year. But what is there to look at in a town like Giarre except mean faces, people who are deep down hungry and call it love.

Roberto and I quarrel often about all this.

"Yes, you're right," he says, "but

it takes time."

What he is really thinking is how he would be better off in Rome where the real money is. When I get angry he shrugs his shoulders, lapses into dialect full of vowel sounds like Arabic, and tells me how I excite him, how he would rather go to bed.

"You don't really care about politics, bella, you need me. I will soothe you."

All right, I slither off with him. He is right but sometimes making love is going off to be slaughtered. Pigs, cows, what a base animal I've become.

Sullen, avoiding the centre of the steps where water runs steadily, cursing the mob of cats sitting trance-like against sodden walls, bored by the prospect of going to meet my inferior lover—awful wet world.

The corso is a tunnel where I clatter along in the grim light of the afternoon. My butcher is busy stuffing sausages, a hot water-bottle stuck in his belt to keep him warm. His hands are terrible pushing pork and anis seeds into shiny membranes. In the grocery Don Vincente is spraying flit. Some of his cats are walking on the counter going after ricotta, some bits of mortadella left in the slicer. He doesn't chase them off, not till the customers come in anyway. I wish I had some appetite, it's such good food when the sun is shining.

"Signora Americana, buona sera," he calls to me. I wish they wouldn't keep greeting me all the time. Can't walk down this street without being saluted twice a day. "Buon giorno" in the morning when I least feel like talking, but one has to answer, "buon Passegio" in the afternoon, they wish you well for everything. "Buona niente," I mumble back, ashamed of myself.

I suppose I am the first person in town to know the sun is back since I do not close my shutters at night. Going to bed is a preparation to enter a tomb. How many times I've avoided Roberto because he can't sleep unless everything is shut tight so that I feel anonymous. In such total darkness there is no telling who is next to you. But an open window is forbidden, one will get a stiff neck or catch a cold. Fresh air belongs outside, so does light. Anyway, how else can you keep out the flies and mosquitoes. Sicily is really the darkest place at night. Bombs have fallen here but windowscreens are unheard of.

Sun. At last.

My maid brings up a plate of strange spiny fruit in celebration.

"Be careful," she says when my son grabs one. Too late, his palm is full of little thorns that will take hours to get out with pincers and some of them will stay in and fester. Concertina opens the prickly pear with three precise gashes and offers me the startling red fruit inside.

"This is practically what we lived on during the war," she explains. "It's full of nourishment but you must be careful not to eat too many. In the war, when there was so little bread, we ate many of these. Sometimes we couldn't defecate for days after."

She shows me how to lift it out of the skin without getting any spina, and to swallow the seed without chewing. Juicy and cool inside, the rain has been good for them.

Later in the day I watch some boys getting this difficult harvest. They tie a tin can to a long stick, cup the tin over the fruit growing out of a large cactus, and snap it off into a bucket. It seems a nervous procedure, especially after all this rain. No matter, the fruit is good, winter is over.

The sight of him wobbles my groin. Desire flares inside me as the sun on my back. Hot as hell and deep like that; red in all my corners, the thick smell of sex everywhere.

We make love like religion. He

lets out my name with his sperm and I feel adored in a way that no virgin has ever been prayed to.

Lapped in waves of good feeling, free and solid my body rises for him. So profound is our contact, today I have forgotten my children. A holiday of the flesh, essential breathing flesh, connective tissue between day and night, before and after love, it's all a rhythm going towards and coming away from actual love which is intercourse.

That in me which can be touched responds only to him. My response is sudden gushes, my inside mucous flesh seems to detach itself from tough walls in an unbelievably painless wave. His very fingerprint is a profound mark on me. Like patterns in the desert that are, after all, the only sign of anything there, it doesn't matter how lasting. If the wind did not stir the sand the desert would have no movement at all.

Thus I lie under this hot Sicilian sun, sweating at last, waiting for more swells and rills.

For weeks cats have disturbed me. Their baby-voiced pain sends me hunting for a child; I think it is my baby screaming.

There are more cats here than people, thinner, wilder, hungrier. At night they rush around in packs, knocking over garbage cans, eating away at anything. They are stronger, more organized in their hunt than the dogs that pad after them. Also in their lovemaking, for dogs look stupid then, as though caught up in something they had nothing to do with. Cats in heat make such a special noise that nights flare into a new season; sleep is given over to the sound of their lust.

Oddly enough, when I finally succeed in watching two cats mate, it is before noon on a hot, clear day. At night they always disappear into corners I cannot find.

There they are, as unaware of the world as I would like to be, deep in an act so mutual it stuns me. Jealous, I wonder about my own sex; surely it is less profound, copulating with Roberto, a fragment of the passion visible here.

The male is much younger and smaller. He has yellow fur, lion crouched on the old female he holds her nape in his teeth, growling moistly, she underneath him all silent, completely held.

He works a long time. My baby tugs at me, wants something. Some women stop and go on quickly, clearly disapproving of my standing there, so openly watching.

"Desgraziata," they say to the cats, certainly to me. For happening there, in front of that American and her child is an act of night, of hiding. I feel very much their hostility, sorry about it, but not enough to stop watching. I like to see animals coupling. It eases memories of my mother and father on sad-sounding beds, sighs dangling into my thin sleep like broken arms. I used to lie in my little room, in my little body, afraid that nothing else existed except that sound and myself listening to it.

The small yellow male jumps off the old female and they both lie down opposite one another, begin to lick and suck and scratch at the wet they have produced.

Down to the beach to feel movement, the fast tough drive down, the sight of water pushing and pulling.

Up in Taormina one never hears the sea, although it is everywhere visible as a remote view pretty and undisturbing. It has no sound at all. Taormina so still, so permanent.

Here at the beach the sea makes noise. The sea here is immediate, contingent on itself. It is change. I watch the tough water, so soft from far away, such a dream of water when you look down at it from that eternal town above.

And here—look how water grows into a killer!

The red flag is run up. A bad current suddenly makes my children struggle in the water. Rocks the size of a child's fist are pulling out from under my feet. Roberto yells to get out of there, keeps on dressing himself.

The waves come in hard and yellow, flat with mud. I grab the children and run up the beach, clutching them like stolen flowers.

Then I take each one for a rest. Lying on top of me, the youngest first, how different they are, how varied their clinging to me. My breasts hurt under their weight but I ask of them an impossible tenderness, pushing them against me this hard is useless, children cannot comfort the mother.

This is my real loneliness—lying on top of me.

We float in a huge grotto, the boat threatened by rocks growing like thorns out of the sea. Black, unwelcoming, the cave goes deep, bats live at the back. But the water is brilliant, looking at it I feel upside down, as if it were sky. So blue that swimming in it would surely leave colour on the skin. But I am afraid to jump in, too radical a place to enter.

Roberto keeps looking at me, watching my nervous face. I keep very still, make my face hard, don't want to show him anything. Why

should he know any more about me; this is a private thing winding among rock thorns, I don't want his comments nor his looks.

"How nervous you are," he says, seeming to like it very much and this makes me feel cold and like his mother. He should not be with me.

I do jump off the boat into that infernal blue, a kind of bravado I detest takes hold of me, forces me towards the end of the grotto where black is waiting. A sudden swell on the water, a motorboat must have passed outside, and I see how far away he is, watching for me, strain showing on his chest where he pushes the oar to steady the boat. I'd better go back, he doesn't swim well enough to save me, would he even try?

My feet scrape on the side of the cave as I turn fast, more afraid than ever now that I sense what a coward he must be. The rock here is purple like a medusa. My son once caught a medusa. Trapped in an empty carton it quivered, really mauve, dangerously beautiful. The afterbirth that oozed out of my body rapidly, I wanted to eat it. It looked more significant than the son just born. The doctor was shocked but he did let me touch it. I was stunned by the look of this glassy, soft flesh that had just left my womb.

The medusa cannot be touched

nor eaten and I have warned my son.

There is my son lying flat on the sand, his legs crossed and swaying. He holds a bar of ice cream high over his head, brings it down for the lick, fans it above his head again, looks at it as it melts and drips in the sun.

He eats that ice cream with the complete concentration available to him at six. At this moment I see my son as he would make love and find him beautiful, as though I had already aged to the time when there would be no more envy, nor any more desire to make him my lover. My fantasy is fabulous. I'm able to imagine the most forbidden. Surely I am a good mother since I know so well when I am not.

The sight of his body reminds me that I can never really touch him.

To eat him is to eat Roberto. Is my lover the son made possible, returned to me, put back in short blasting thrills, without that pain I bore so well?

Roberto has driven into me like a corkscrew; I cannot disengage myself without losing essential pieces. In these hot patches of afternoon, light and heat gather into direct touch. He becomes light and heat itself, welling around me in absolute contact. Myself turned inside out spills away at him. I am the beach where he ebbs and tides. Windless days moving only in my belly.

Yet nothing gets finished. Sick grows my lust. I feel afraid but it's only here, buried inside this Sicilian tomb, that I can conceive of death, perhaps accept it as the only dignified craving.

Hot light of the Sicilian sun hits me like a rock. Through the window I see the woman next door washing her endless sheets. An ugly creature who screams her way into my life every morning so that I hate right away. No way to wake up except hating noise and light and the things in the room that I can't see clearly because of my bastard eye-sight.

She is threatening; her bulk a black hole in the sky. I pull up the blanket to cover that red hole I've become.

All this terror because of my eyes, hysterical vision, blurred, every small light an immense fire, her sheets ride at me in flags, pointing to the prostitute sleeping late.

In the bathroom I look closely at what she might have seen. A frightened, nostalgic search for the gaudy object of the night before; the mirror returns an ugly result of a thin, strained face with spider dreaming eyes, so magnificent at night when she paints herself for the part. Black light not caused by drugs as her friends suspect. Caused by what then? All her fevers.

Yes, Regina of the night, a huge flower nearly a foot in diameter, blooming only in the night. Profoundly open, showing a vast white depth, as I show black in my deep myopic eyes. Startling to wind around dark streets and find this giant growing, opening. By day a wilted mess of long hanging, worn petals.

That bitch over there, scrubbing her virtue while a tense Sicilian song screams out of her, going past me to the neighbours waiting for her message like savages.

Swimming today was unpleasant, the water too warm.

Scooping my hands through the soft wet, of a sudden I held a medusa. Frantically I let go, shaking away the feel of it. Then I looked down at the vague rocks below, hating my weak eyes. I would always be afraid of it down there. Why not, I couldn't see it. A low pressure feeling made my body heavy, swimming was hard, a tunnel to be dug.

Roberto spread on the sand in an odd, passive position. "Molto pederaste," I tease, standing over him, stealing light.

"Why do you put shadows in front of me," he complains, sliding away in the luxuriant way of a man who pleasures deeply in sex, gives his man milk freely. A passive gladiator, knowing himself to be potent at will.

"Oh bella, what could be better?" he asks.

"All that which isn't," I answer him.

For him there is nothing casual about sex, it is an absolute and absorbing experience. How it tires and thrills me. I sit inside this rainbow of sensations like a supersensitive doll, lost but watching. I feel that I control him, that our copulating is an art exercised by me. I need only to use certain gestures and he swoons. My effect on him makes me swoon.

Then I forget him and listen to the termites eating the bed that holds us.

Summer is a violent presence. Too hot now to drive to the beach. I scold my children into the cool house, annoyed by their energy. My son kills flies while the baby pokes at ants. Her milk sours in the glass.

The streets are quiet, a fierce glare on the pavement. In the distance Etna looks ordinary without snow.

The maid uses her umbrella to go shopping. I worry what will please the children. So hard to eat anything in this heat except fruit and vegetables. The best thing is melon, a huge speckled kind with a ruby centre. We are all thinner from this diet. Only way to tolerate this weather is to sleep all day and sit in the cafe evenings. Then the piazza is alive again with frantic children. There's no use putting them to bed before eleven, much too hot. My maid wets down the pillow under her head.

"This is nothing," she sighs, "wait till the scirocco blows."

I wish I had the energy to leave here.

Scirocco wraps me in a humid trance. The fish on the beach called Molla, at first I thought it was the fin of a great fish but there it lay, being all of it, really small and dead and grey. Touching it was such a mistake, all slime, with the most sticky smell. I kept digging my fingers into the sand, trying to scrape off the smell, the matter.

Just so is the scirocco fast on me. I sit in space padded by that kind of slime the fish had, the muck that jellyfish are made of.

I look at it all. The sea, the rocks, people; just objects. I'm afraid I will sit like this in another country waiting for a sense of importance, lying, manipulating, to bring back a sense of life. There is no sense leaving here for there is always that formidable silence, that sitting so still that I do better than anyone else, while inside me is movement. I think and think, my hands paralyzed, eyes gone far, staring blind the horizon.

I have sat like this a long time, in a fever of silence. Inside my face is hard, aching tension. All my life stirs in me, pushing at me, begging to be let out.

This seems to be my new madness.

I need this piazza with its lack of view, only sky against which trees hold still and the lanterns flare into several moons. There is only that, and myself on the other side of it.

Now the heat and the mountain are together, fire and size closing up my view. The sky is thick with scirocco and never blue.

As Clarita loved blue with her sapphire ring and the blue, man-tailored suits and blue eyes that I wanted to eat as I have eaten the eyes of carp my mother cooked for me. Who watched me eat the head of the fish and there was no disgust only approval of my taste. The tongue of the fish milky soft, the eyes gelatin soft, soft heads of fish, my mother's eyes love soft on her happy-eating child.

As I wish now to lick the eyes of

Roberto because there is nothing disgusting about him. Clarita spoiled my pleasure when she watched me eat the head of the carp. She felt disgust and gave it to me. But Roberto has renewed my desire to eat eyes. I want his. The appetite more important than the eating and thus I know that I am not yet mad. The head of a fish and the head of a man—I still know the difference.

As there is no separation here between sky and water and mountain; it's all together in a humid blur, put before me on this piazza where those few trees still stupidly produce florist-size flowers, dropping into coffee cups. Those trees will never be a forest, will never know the difference.

I realize now how lonely the metaphor; when Roberto was inside me I said: "You are a tree inside me."

For days the air has been too heavy. In cool countries it's this way before a storm but there is no rain for Sicily in August.

Roberto keeps checking the mountain. "That's where it's coming from," he says thoughtfully, "You'll see something happen very soon," he adds, as though he is planning a special gift for me.

And it does. Etna goes into full eruption. A sudden, dull boom calls for attention. There, in a dark moonless sky, twenty kilometres away, the volcano pours and roars out the fire inside it. Hundreds of feet in the air the flames shoot straight up, red as forever.

The town is awake, this hasn't happened in years, not this strong. The air is better now, some of the pressure gone.

I show my children what they have never seen before.

"Are we all going to burn, Mama?"

"No," I answer softly, "it's too far away."

But inside me there is a great fear along with terrific excitement; my body is very hot as though it were a huge erection.

I am so confused by this erupting landscape, I rush towards Roberto who receives me proudly as though he has made this happen. I look for some sense of order, everything appears hot and smolten together. What is male or female anymore? What am I doing with an erection? Oh yes, it's his! But I feel the potent one.

Etna continues to erupt. News of it is in all the papers of the world. Relatives send me telegrams to see if we are all right. Of course we are at this distance, but I feel troubled. The sight of lava boiling down a mountainside, even miles away, is not simple.

My lovemaking is affected. Some nights I only want to be kissed; it's everything to me. In a kiss there is no finishing, only constant hunger and constant eating. Making love is finite; somebody, some organ tires. But in my mouth is every desire and I feel the juice and the teeth and the deep smell of the person I kiss and whose longing for me I suck into me.

Roberto is bewildered yet he follows the contours of my temperament as though I were the mountain we are both excited by.

I begin to despise his lack of protest. His tolerance of me is flaccid, I cannot respect a man who will permit me every caprice. Kissing is not enough, he should know that, should rape me.

After many days of intense, pointed heat the eruption subsides. The climate is radically changed; summer seems over. I long for clean empty cold, so necessary to my burdened self. But winter from here is a rare feat, even in my imagination.

Fretting away time, swinging on people's talk, grasping their faces like fruit falling; a poor harvest, nothing like the appetite inside me.

A blind man passes, blowing on a flute, making sounds so high, hurting, but really music. My breathing stops along with his; together we go to the same high, thrilling place.

But the six o'clock light in the piazza is toneless, not blue. Seven oleander trees sticking out, dusty, always quiet trees, I never see them move. Wrought iron trees, they might as well be the same species as the lanterns near them.

I put some money in his hand and beg him to play on. He does, his Sicilian face bent over complicated sounds, his face down dragged, trying to please me. But it's difficult to breathe, all the dull green, old, nonmoving growth of Sicily is here in this piazza, in these seven trees. Sound becomes just that and I am no longer interested.

I walk away, out of town, towards the low hills stretched out like a chain of cemeteries. The dead green colour; no real green, just shades of black, especially the cypresses, black ties of mourning worn by men, the priest-coloured trees.

How annoyed I am, sensing my own fatigue in the tired presence of this ancient country. With those women staring at me, ill shadowed faces pressed against the window of the door, the only source of light. Fat, pale women, engorged from bad food, a bland shortlived look in

182

their eyes. Visions of their dusty organs that will someday dry up and peel away from them like the paint on their decayed houses.

They sit alone or in smudged groups, sewing on their dowries of gorgeous bedsheets. This is the only passion allowed them before marriage, the linen they will bring to the eventual husband must be the finest, scrolled with such tiny stitches that it takes a month just to embroider the edges.

Nearly all wear mourning, their sex gored by black dresses making the curves of them look empty, all wrong. Barbaric religion with its loud, dimestore rites, at the innumerable fiestas these camouflaged women carry wooden saints like lovers, fireworks blasting away the little money earned, on their faces the bang bang joy of childish sacrifice.

Immense boredom that forces me into the manufacture of intrigue, of false sentiment. Grabbing the looks of strangers, finding here a nose, there a mouth that pleases. And the women looked at by me, the sudden man. That lovely Italian girl. I said she is the pillow of a bed and had to explain that it meant the softest, the best part of the bed, of lying down. A woman's face like a soft sigh of relief.

Roberto sitting alongside me in this fog of sex. We do nothing but invent each other's perversities. I am dutifully degenerate, but my face is false; not passionate with desire, but passionate with a desire to feel. Yet there is this thickness, this awareness of sexual importance. The mountain hovers, girls pass, each one appraised and filed away by both of us in a special safety vault of flesh.

This theatrical doom, this smear of a landscape so tired of living, of reproducing itself, having lost all vital organs. Only some desire left and that old, antiquely worn, a patina of what was. A tired stage with pointless drama. Scrub, flowers, no real trees just the worn spears of cypresses.

And yet I feel important here. I have a role, my mirror is Roberto who values all that in me which he cannot name but finds in my bed where I give him, because I can still do that, so much loveliness. Inside me there is something sensitive with many feelers like an octopus, nervous star of the sea.

What happened today except that I laid my head on the legs of Pino.

I had just been swimming, felt a great energy in the water like a bird flying. The water a deep, dangerous sky. Outside the bay the water

incredibly cold, made my urine come hot and slow and I lay still to let it happen.

A feeling of rest afterwards, lying against him on the beach, pebbles on my thighs sticking hard, creating ugly toad skin in marvellous colours. I was sure nothing else would happen to me that day; it had all gone in the water.

Roberto up in town, working. He is certainly not jealous of Pino, a homosexual. "You need friends," he says, making pitifully clear his limited function in my life.

I spend hours with Pino. Meeting

184

him is seeing a real shape in a cloud and then watching it disperse. He looks like a man, I cannot believe him when he talks about men, it must all be a trap to make me love his soul. For there is love between us but we touch only with words and certain concentrated looks. I feel a special fear lying on a part of him that belongs to his body. One of us is virgin; I cannot afford to long for him, there is something so deep and erotic between us that any contact can only magnify its impossible dimensions.

Talking with him makes me feel large, round, swollen with white light. "Tonight at two o'clock the moon will be full. Try and get away from him." He says this, he who has the moon inside him in big flat circles.

There is my baby twirling her white towel around her in a moon circle. She doesn't know how much I watch her. Thinking about Pino I absorb her complete sanity and am grateful, I think also of Roberto standing so concretely somewhere in his bar. I certainly love those two simple creatures, experience them in the same way.

But Pino with his insistent intellect draws me to him. "You're just using Roberto," he says. "You don't love him."

"I can love many people all at the same time."

"Perhaps, but your love is in pieces, broken into three."

Of course I know what he means but he is only waiting for me to lose my sex while I wait to see his. In the meanwhile he's revolting. All his physical processes annoy me in small definite beats; just the way he is sucking an orange, juice dribbling on his hairless chest. I recall Roberto on whose body hair grows like experience.

This queer, with his snaky mouth enveloping food, his toenails are enormous, his arms too short. Touching him would be grey as brain skin.

And yet, what must he feel in my presence, he who is so much more delicate than I am. Of course he is homosexual, it's spilled on him like wine, enhancing but also sour. I long for one straightforward person. Really only children please me now. I am becoming saturated with sex. I shall need a retreat soon.

When the moon is full I visit Pino in his room. He looks so destroyed, lying on a bed, dressed in ugly clothes which make him look washed up. He does so want to be picked up and put together again. In his body, by me.

As I find him there, strewn on that bed, I worry, afraid he'll make a move towards me. I cannot desire him because he is man-woman and I only want simple loving, shape of tulip, penis flower.

"You want everything," he says, as though this is wrong of me. But surely he says this because he can give me so little, that pervert.

Like the eruption of Etna, when I saw too much light, I feel affected by him, confused.

"You're my first Eve," he continues, and I feel disgust at a confession he should make to his mirror since he is his own woman. Pino is every gender put into one body, badly twisted, depressing because of its complex shape. A body should be plain. Being with him makes me swollen in an unnatural way, not at all like being pregnant, my body then a great rich avocado.

Even his mouth is in sections, long snaking over words, and kissing him is kissing parts. Shame rises in me now in the clearest fashion, shame not desire forces me into this impossible pose. I lie crumpled on his bed, part of the particular debris around him. Not a place for sleep here, full too full of books and terrible ripped pages of poetry, where has he gotten all those? Everyone who has ever written lies on his bed, he knows too much, reads to me while the moon hovers

dangerously near the window. I know nothing compared to him but he does not know it's shame over my poor exploited body that keeps me from him. I can only think of the perfect athletes he is used to while his head longs for me. But if I am to be his first woman love then I must be perfect and I am not. Thoughts of Roberto who sucks even my toes and becomes potent with the sight of my soft, tired breasts, my mother scars. Fairies only know love in the front or love in the back. Pino fouls my idea of myself. Lousy queer, young and childless, without anything, just the idea of me in his head.

Finally we touch somewhere. He fingertips across my hair which goes limp under his hand. I wonder whether he desires me now or whether he just wants to see how I am made.

Vaguely aggressive his odourless body near me is a thorn spread out as he lays himself flat against me. I follow his position and we are two people in the same coffin.

"I must go."

"You're so incomplete," he accuses, but I do get up, nauseated by this long evening. Later on I will push my face into Roberto, glad to get his smell. His sweat is something good coming at me, his very exudations are appetizing, just as my children's bodies are completely edible, my appetite for the four of them never diminishes.

Now just the face of Pino is left, full sad before me as I prepare to leave, exposed as for a death-mask. He has the air of someone in constant preparation for suicide. But I have enough of him, must leave. His head is separate from his body; he is in pieces and I will not help him. Loving cannot be talked about. He is wrong about everything below his head and his body went away from him a long time ago.

Electric light busts the leaves and palm trees split the sky while we sit in this garden and talk. He is a bottomless pit, graining the landscape. The garden full of ignored flowers in oppressive abundance. No smell at all, only appearance. Field and country unknown here, wailing with cats and dogs in each of which I see my own peculiar disfigurement, depending on the degrees of sadness that makes me either shrug or cry.

With Pino I am frankly sad, allow my face to ugly away. My hair is tight in brain-pulling hurt; I confront with him open suffering. Which he does not believe in. Or does not find sufficient.

"Do you ever tell the truth, or rather do you ever feel the truth?"

he asks, his black milk eyes staring into me and I am glad that he does not have as many eyes as the limbs of an octopus. Yet he sucks at me in the same way and I become fish caught, human eaten.

Oh this garden, with that face exposed like an over-ripe melon. Clarita, when she tired of me, threw me away from her like rotten fruit.

Pino is quiet, looking down, deep lines frame his snake mouth. In his swamp of thought he waits for me but my body is right, my mother was a peasant, once she was thick and blood fresh. I saw her working in another garden, a long time down, her animal health leg-spread over the hot growth she tended. It doesn't matter now about her change, the smell of nasturtiums still puts me in a swoon of remembrance.

Here in Sicily I eat the flower itself and come that much closer to the smell of it and I chew at the memories of other beaches where I gathered pieces of amber to save forever but have lost.

I grab at the flowers, at my mother who took care of me then on the white sweet sand. I roll in the smell of her orange love, thick inside the dear flesh of her palms that curve me round with bliss.

Now my own children are the face I wanted to be and I wait for their deep sleeping when I thieve away at those round open faces, finding my mother's love in giving to them. Do finally get full, in feeding I am fed.

Day hazes into night. The flesh trap opens and I fall under Roberto's body. The hair on his chest is so many sculpted flowers. My hand traverses a forest, indescribably mine. I suck at his nipples as at a female fountain held up by a phallus. "I'll split you open with my penis," he says, a passion in his voice that heats me and makes me obey.

When will this end? The pleasure I find with Roberto is wrong, he is not my peer. My talks with Pino have brought me back somewhat; I have loved a better person. But I want Roberto's body, worried over wanting an animal. Never have I gone so against my grain. Why can't I love the right man with all my red flesh? This little man with the delicious skin, I would so much like to respect him. And do not. And continue to sleep with him.

"Your sex is an illusion," says Pino, and I don't know anymore, he has blurred me. Who will save me, will bring me the word? Who will tell me that making love is honest. I do love Roberto if love means everything, including dis-

grace. His body and mine together are love concrete. Before and after we are dogs and cats, vulgarity and boredom. I do not esteem him.

But the trap shuts hard, banging at me a message that says only this moment, this movement is the truth.

"Stop seeing so much of Pino."

"You said I need friends."

"People are talking."

"Everyone knows he is queer."

"He is still a man."

"You flatter me."

"Bitch, don't play with me!" and Roberto slaps me in the face. "You know I've been patient with you. But don't make me appear a cornuto in front of my friends."

"So that's your problem, not whether I'm faithful to you, but whether your friends think so."

"You can't understand us. You are a foreigner."

"I'm glad. I don't want your problems. You have stupid problems, you think everything is sex."

"Without sex there is nothing."

My face burns. Really quite pleasant. He looks beautiful, anger comes straight at me like an arrow from a bow. A terrific flush of desire takes me to the nearest wall where I spread myself out as his target.

Goodbye to Pino.
I offered him my hand in the

most furtive, fleeting way. He had no time at all to say anything. I did not want him to speak; everything had ended for us. The rest could only be sentiment and lecture.

I cannot forget the startled eyes, the clear pain staring at me, at my cowardly farewell. The fool I'd made of him in loving me.

I left him abruptly as I had done so many times in his house. But this was the last and he knew it and ached from it; I only felt impressed by the expression in his eyes.

There sit the two brothers in front of me. Made of the same flesh, one more beautiful, both with thick graceful skin that I want to bite. I wish to have them both lust for me and put me in bed between them. Imagine two brothers bursting over the same woman!

This perversity is clearly confined to my imagination. If Roberto knew that I even thought about his brother he would probably beat me. A woman belongs only to one man in his country. His brother hardly ever speaks to me for fear of arousing any suspicion. If he cares for me at all, and I think he does, his every intention is to leave his brother's woman alone. Someday I hope to meet him in another country.

Sicily, old, with a tough sense of order. A story in the paper of a woman whose husband was killed. She knew the killer but would not tell the police. She merely pointed to her belly, swollen with child, and said: "He knows, and will attend to it someday."

Vendetta. When I am bad with Roberto he just stretches out his hand, bobs it up and down lightly. The gestures carries a gentle but very precise warning.

Yet I happen only here in the place I resent. Sicily manures me into being. If I could only respect the fruit of me. Rotten, complicated bloom of sex, exaggerated as the flower of a cactus.

Tired, all juiced out. I'm thinner, very fatigued. The doctor recommends an analysis of my blood. But it's all this fornicating that's draining me. Nothing else is any good, or good enough, only with him can I stop thinking. I don't even dare sleep; my dreams are weary reminders that I have no other recourse.

My mother an octopus. Many arms coming out of the very centre, all grabbing me to her soft parts where she may, I permit it, chew me, use me up. I am now the octopus, mucus, held together by soft moist membrane, suckering

everywhere. Dreams of unending hunger, interrupted by sleep. I have many mouths and only in the suck-feel attachment of my tentacles do I feel in contact, my reach is long and bizarre. I shudder at the cold touch of many arms that I never wanted to grow but only to have around me from another source.

I find myself like pressed flowers in an old book, dry and faded, an ugly trace of what was once wild and juicy. I look for water to fill me, I drink and swim, Japanese flowers that grow in water and become something. I dive as deep as I can but come up dehydrated.

There is that glossy sun again, open above me like a naked body, while in this Sicily those secret pubic hills keep on and on, hiding from me. Are they attics and cellars I crept around in with my school-friends as we jabbed and scratched into our child bodies looking for hair and holes and black sex. My inside felt exhausted, the dull worn green of Sicilian earth, not growing anymore—only there.

How long is desire when given time enough, Sicily enough?

I wait for an end to this degrading passion. I wish he did not exist, while the sight of him, his teeth, his glittering eyes, grapes spit out, fish bones, his urine, all that is produced by his body excites me.

There are moments of hatred between us, we drift into a mean way, I've reduced him to an exasperated state. He slaps me around, spits. And I need this humiliation in order to feel. Only crisis provokes me.

What will happen to him when I am gone? For I shall get out of this. I am complex, capable of many excitements, a sensual intellectual, and he has also made me beautiful. Never have I looked so well, surely this is the last ripening, my flower fall, myself a ripe fruit in fall. Where to land, where to conceive further?

And he will be left behind to idle away his life in stupid innocence, unwilling to grant me evil, believing that my usage of him has been love. Yet now, while I am here, I am committed to him; a witch ensnared by a fool.

Exposed to myself as that small beach where we wait for a tide that is never high enough. The filth of the Mediterranean remains, more obvious now because of the clean edge.

Roberto is deep in thought and does not feel the wave that spreads over his feet making them shine.

Earlier we argued; he saw me

flirting with some tall Swede. I do it on purpose; his jealousy excites me for I am at that point where any effort is an interruption in the blank day, that vuoto where nothing happens except when it is beaten into me. I've become the big lax mouth and even ugly food is chewed at; disgust itself becomes something felt, more interesting than ordinary pleasure, pushed down my throat so there is no choice.

"Suck me here," he says and I do, pleased by the command, the actual revulsion layered over by months of effort to be sexually enormous.

"Lick me," and I, aware of my lying face, cannot avoid my duty because I too can see my passionate face in the pupils of his love-frantic eyes. I have conned this boy with my liar charm—I suck and lick and sigh while he is truly involved with a woman he has never expected to love. Small animal that he is, smaller than his emotions, laid across her in tiring ceremony.

"Are you satisfied now, do you still need some one else?"

"Maybe tomorrow," I taunt.

He rolls away from me and goes to sleep. The small beach is dull. I look at the terraced hump of fields behind, a chewed out skyline. Eyes pale in my head; I am not curious.

Ruin of a castle, built by the

Saracens, it decays above the town in toothy outline. Not splendid anymore, just a good place to take the children where we play hide and seek.

"Where are you, Mama," yells the middle one, a girl who looks like a happy version of me. What a disgusting woman I am behind the mother she loves.

I bury myself in the shadows of the castle, wanting to delay her discovery of me. To the west lies Etna, no longer active, nothing but a shadow now, as thin as the dark I'm hiding in. "If only you'd keep on blowing up," I think, "it would keep me moving, anything is better than this dry burden of myself."

It's cold leaning against that dark wall. I'm tired of this game. Why doesn't she find me or is it save me? Yes, my children will save me, they are my only weapon.

How long it seems till she comes, her voice screams closer, "Mama, I'll get you, wait, wait . . ." breaks off in laughter at the sight of me. Her hand is warm pulling me into the sun, her trophy.

One cloud in the whole sky, exactly like wet cotton. There is no wind and that white blob stays there, nearly inside the mouth of Etna. I am determined to sit it out, surely the cloud will move on, nothing up there should be so still, large as a nightmare when the vomit kept heaving up from the bottom of me.

Alone in the night of my mother's garden, my suffering real, visible in spit and bile and tears. She's not there to wipe it off, gone the soft cotton of her breasts. Agony looking at that sky with the stinking stars, burning down to me the first knowledge of infinity. Everything small and close and warm gone; my mother an abstraction.

I see her in the mountains of Sicily, a face in the dry tough hills where olive trees shrug off indecently small fruit. The age of these trees darker than the Greek ruins spread about here like ordinary facts; history is a carpet to walk on, marble columns are flowers I ignore. My lament is not general—I want only my mother.

The cloud hangs over me. I watch it hopelessly like a mystic fixed on the wrong object. A false symbol as is false my love with Roberto. But I want everything now, my greed established from the very beginning, the mark on my forehead pressed deep by my mother's blundering, blameless hand.

Lusting for a red split mountain but this is not a mountain of a man. He is caving in, his soft parts eroded from my excessive want. "Let me rest a while, it will come back," he sighs, useless next to me.

I go to the bathroom and try, with very cold water, to wash away my affliction. Downstairs some child is coughing in his sleep but I don't have the energy to go see who it is. I'm the one in trouble.

When I am back in bed he puts his head on my breasts where I allow him to remain. He clings to me in the passive way of a helpless child who already dislikes his mother.

"I'm sorry," he mumbles, "As soon as I'm rested I'll go home."

"Don't worry," I answer politely, feeling free of him. If he were suddenly dead it wouldn't matter to me.

"Do you think I should see a doctor?"

"Why don't you wait and see if it happens again."

"Yes, that's true, it's only the first time."

He gets up, dresses with excessive care. "My impotent dandy," I think, "I use you like flowers in a room, distracting from the white wall."

He stands by the window, taller now in his shoes. He says, "You have a beautiful view of my country," his voice too loud in my empty room.

"Hurry up, I want to see the children."

"But they're asleep, they don't need you."

Intensely nervous I snarl, "What do you know about their dreams?"

"I'll see you tomorrow when you feel better," and he tiptoes out, in his exit all the cowardice I've suspected in him.

Etna erupts again, but it's a stale event, I've seen it before. Seen by day the fire is weak, a dull red. Let the tourists gape at it, I think, and remain in the cafe where parts of strangers' faces rock me in the maze of my past.

I sit in this cooling land. Summer is over, my passionate swimming gone dry. Dogs I no longer love straggle across the piazza.

This is a ride on a badly lit bus taking me from an unhappy place to an indifferent one. Going home from school was like this, not really sad, just pale, lifeless. I felt like the other passengers looked. We were all poorly made statues coming alive at stops and starts, disliking one another.

A certain sleep is riding me, a doze like the underlit bus I've known.

Roberto noses at me with regained confidence. He bullies me

into feeling something, but it's flat, my body responds to a habit. He bores me, the town bores me; I've understood everything. This idolatry of a human body—where does magic begin anymore?

The bed is soft, too soft; the covers heavy on me, too warm—but warm. Outside the air is a hostile mass, inside this bed the heat I crave is mixed with his particular flesh. Has no one ever loved me like this? Is that the clue? He wants to give me his blood; I will let him.

Again he is a gorgeous statue all mine, lost in me. I am absorbed by the hard penis and the soft red wet of his mouth. How difficult it would be to lie alone in the wind outside . . . He does mean something to me after all, he is my deepest physical sense, the one I least understand, or least satisfy, or most—I don't know even this anymore.

Sloppy drunk, the corso yawns ahead like a tunnel, I push on, the hell with walls, I just want to get through.

"Guarda la Americana," I hear in the shops. My condition is obvious and I don't care, I wipe my hands along the windows just for spite.

I feel bad, crippled, the sky a near dampness in my bones. I ache; wrong colour on the walls, the narrow street is one big stone.

Finally the arch that opens to the piazza. I need coffee, Italian coffee stuck into me like an injection of energy.

There's Roberto, my little horse, sitting all tight and vanished in himself, waiting among the bad sounds, his voice harsh in greeting: "Ubriaga, sit down before you fall."

That voice, low, of a small man, bent against pedlar songs more powerful than his. The fish dart of vulgar speech drones at me: "Cattive," he hisses, and pulls me into a chair. People are staring, "Your children should see you now."

I've heard that. Now I sit still, in false dignity, on the auction block of this market where I have sold myself to undignified pleasure. He fills my vagina as I fill time, waiting for an end.

So it's possible to adore legs and shoulders, the place where teeth are set. Look at him, what a passionate ornament he is. Anger and frustration have coloured him into a man. He's holding onto my arm as though it were his. Having lost respect for all else, what remains? Only parts of the body. What a limited cult. Here I am on my knees in filth, praying over a groin.

Can one survive without killing?

I need his death as I need health.

The real disgrace is in the drink poured down during the act of disgracement.

"Look at you, you haven't even washed your feet for me."

"Get me a drink."

"Wash your feet."

"Spit on them."

I drag out of bed, wipe up his saliva, my body naked as a cross.

"What a beautiful back you have anyway," he says in a forgiving way.

A long pull at the bottle to help swallow this merda. Then a pill, enzyme to digest the merda, colour of dirty tongue licking away at my self esteem, whatever that was, I can't remember. There are only traces of something I recall and which continue to feel heavy. But lick, suck, squeeze away loneliness; hate is better than an empty bed.

After such love—oh mother, forgive me—my body lies in a crazy heap. Head splitting, eyes breaking open, afraid to look. But also afraid to lose this mad pattern, it does interest me, it does eat time. Pour down more drink, another pill, avoid health for it may mean death. Certainly someone will have to be eliminated.

Oh my fantastic affliction, are you feeling weak? What can I give you now, or what will you take away from me? Who will I be when you leave, and where are you going? ·

To my children?

I hate you. I shall destroy you, not Roberto.

Oh children, do not open the door if I am not your mother.

I send my maid away for a few days, hoping that work will put a straight-jacket around me.

She will visit her family in a hill-town close by where the harvest is on. "Come on Sunday with the children, I'll show you how we press the wine."

"Yes, I want to see that, want to see new things."

"But where is she going, Mama, who will take care of us?"

"I will, of course."

"Oh you're always tired, or visiting friends."

I look at them, aghast at how far things have gone.

"Well, I was tired for a while, now I'm o.k. and we'll have fun."

They still believe in me. Together we set the house in order, go shopping. I feel well protected walking down the very street where I stumbled so recently. "I'll make you pancakes for supper just like in America."

We buy strawberry jam and lots of apples, hard and yellow, grown on the slopes of Etna. Don Vincente gives each of the children a candy.

We scatter on down the corso, nothing seems to get in the way. Through the arch and into the big golden piazza where I lose them like balloons.

I rest on the steps of the cathedral and watch them play. Across the street I see Roberto working over the cash register. He beckons to me but I gesture no, no, too busy with the children.

He comes over with some cakes for each of them. My son declines, "Yeah, I know, now you'll just talk to him and we won't have any fun."

"Don't be silly," I answer, "Take the cake and let's go on to the giardino publico."

Safe among them in the public garden. It's a formal tropical garden like a painting by Rousseau. All kinds of flowers, even daisies lushed out into trees. Nothing is small,

hibiscus the size of a hand, trumpet flowers, flesh-thick, grown to man-eating size, with a smell so deep. They say if you sleep under them you can never wake up.

The sun is digging at me, tiring and complicating my view of this Sicilian growth repulsive with overproduction. Never dying but also never beginning, it's a still place where I have seen hills retain the same colour for nearly a year, a dreadful green, lacking all vitality.

In the middle of it all stands Etna, the top of her black, bare as a bone. "Look at the mountain," my daughter says. "It must be very thirsty."

Sunday morning we drive to Granite, a town built on the rock it's named for. A bleached succession of stone huts blending into the background like rubble.

Concertina, very clean and glad to see us. Her mother and father shake my hand in a formal way. He's old and small, a tough remnant of a man. He leads us into the house, and we all sit down at a large table. The mother cuts some rude bread. We drink a toast with wine that's almost blue it's so strong.

Then it's quiet. A lot of flies gather around us. The old woman scatters them away from the bread. I am shocked by the many creases in the palm of her hand, as though she's cut herself too often.

Concertina shows us the house, steps leading to the plain room where she was born. She opens a wooden trunk and counts through the linen she has prepared for a dowry. "What a lucky husband you will have," I say to show my appreciation. It's pleasant to be here; these are kind people who see no evil in me and so I have none.

We talk about America, look at pictures of relatives who live there. The mother has me describe the subway, "Yes, yes, just like our bus when it goes through a tunnel." She shivers, "It's so cold then."

I look around at their belongings. So little else except the beds, the table. The kitchen is merely a recess in the main room, with charcoal fire and some water in a pitcher. One large, highly coloured religious scene is the ornament on the wall which is painted a pale cold blue. These people could move out of here with very little fuss. On this quiet Sunday poverty seems an attractive state.

Later we all walk down the miserly street to the tavern. In the back room, on a platform, some boys are stamping on a pile of grapes with bare feet. It's very damp and cold, their feet are blue, toenails black from the stain of grapes.

The juice runs off the platform

198

into a barrel from where it will be strained and poured into bottles. The smell is terrific, fresh and sour at the same time.

In the gloom of this cavern the boys treading look like prisoners. They are young unhealthy creatures, they make the sunlight we've come from a memory.

My children are restless. I buy some tepid Coca Cola to drink in the bright street. My son drops his bottle and some dogs rush over to lap at the mess.

"Let's go to the oil press," Concertina suggests.

We continue down the street, dogs following, in each doorway some people are staring at us.

Another cave with a large wooden press with more boys turning it. I wonder what happened to the men in this town. I feel ill from the rancid odour, the viscous product looks dreadful.

"We must be getting back," I tell the maid. "You'd better get ready."

"But my mother has a meal for you."

"Good, the children must be very hungry."

We go back to the house and I try to eat the pasta heavy with oil and tomatoes. "I'm sorry, Signora, my stomach is not good today, forgive me if I don't finish."

"You must make your lady some camomile tea when you get home, Concertina."

The maid looks at me strangely.

On the way back, the baby falls asleep in her arms. I feel sad and jealous, wish I were going back without the maid so the baby would have just me again.

I drive too fast, want to get finished with this dreary ride. Approaching Taormina, the lights of the town glow like pearls in the dusk, a necklace of wealth awaits us up there.

The piazza is lush with people in Sunday clothes. The church door is wide open, an elegant light streaming out as from the lobby of a great hotel.

The cafe is full of Sicilians from Messina. They always come on Sunday night to have a treat, to look at tourists. As I enter the terrace, pushing my way through ample families eating ice cream, drinking sodas, I feel a hundred curious eyes on me. Fortunately I've put on a skirt and some high heels, it just won't do to wear pants and sandals on these nights, it makes me more of an oddity than I already am with my straight hair and pale lips. Anyway, a woman is not considered "elegante" unless she is dressed the way they are. I've not been able to convince Roberto that to be casual is to be chic, he'll approve of my costume tonight, I'm sure.

Finally I see him, way in the back, watching over the waiters as they carry trays out of the kitchen.

He looks nasty and busy; I suppose I ought to come back later when there's less work but I want to be near him. The sight of him makes me feel heavy, not in a good way but complex, too full of something.

"So you're back for more," he mocks, not standing up to greet me. My excitement falls apart like a badly wrapped package. There's nothing inside me now except the awareness of fraud. I feel ugly as he looks me up and down.

"You look very tired from all your hard work, maybe you'd better sit down here," he adds in a bland voice.

I realize then that he is play-acting, he is trying to hide his pleasure at having me back. But who can pay the price for this tawdry bit of theatre except myself?

That night I watch his eyes go flat, absolutely under my reign, while his body over me is sodden with joy at mounting me again.

I have a squalid sense of victory. I do not desire him, all this now is patience on my part, an animal loneliness and also a kind of whoredom. Next, thinks a whore; next,

think I.

Clearly the fever in this unlovely affair is in the vulgarity. Truce, calm found only in bed after the act. A bad calm, full of knowledge that this sweet exhaustion is momentary, that in the daytime our ugly tempers will muck all that went before. But the fight is unfair; I am superior even though I seem to lose. I allow him to win as soon as I feel his stark, desperate love. For I am sure that the only tender moments in his life are with me. Underneath his dreadful breeding, inside the heart of this merchant there is a soft man, seen only by me, his first love.

I am his bread in a starved country where he was taught to distrust gentleness. "Only a jufa, a fool, gives to a beggar what he himself might use some day."

He says this and shows me trunks of clothes he can no longer wear, stacks of junk that he can't throw away because some of it might be useful someday. "Someday," this is the slogan of Sicily, decrepit from centuries of vengeance, where fear of the Mafia is greater than the fear of God.

This flesh bath is growing tepid. I begin to smell him. Horrid pre-occupation with new details of him, smells, gestures. Even as I use him night after night the judgement of him continues. The decline brings nastiness but I savour it; survival is an ugly struggle. Success is in one more tentacle to make me more fit in this complicated world. I am an octopus swimming off in a new direction, quickly, so that my arms will not pull me to pieces inside the trap.

Watching him eat, I really must leave the table. Terrible mixing of foods in his mouth, eating with such concentration. That which makes him exciting in bed oddly enough makes him intolerable in common life. Real gluttony. How vulgar this insistence on doing only what he is doing, as though he has killed the rest of life. He gorges himself, is made nervous and sick by his appetite. He cannot accept more than what he can hear or touch. There is so much more, but he is afraid.

He washes, washes before and after love, keeping busy, shutting out the afterward, which is for me the only reality. What I do with him, what he considers the real present, I think of as a lapse in me, a jump towards earth in a dubious parachute, longing for the solid creaking plane above me ploughing through an abstract beautiful sky, arriving nowhere—but having been everywhere.

It's true that I needed him to fill the blank present. But to love him could never hurt me because I never valued him. My investment was small, worth a piece of skin only organ deep. I can cut him out as one can cut the genitals of a man—as one can never cut off the real, slow sadness of thought.

My past is a train that he has boarded and it is here that I sever myself from him. As we sit under the same motion, while I think, he picks his feet and reads the paper. Nearly everything passes by him. He does not sink into the gloom produced by motion which must be felt if one is more than animal. He knows only that life is inconvenient while for me the train keeps on, the view moves and I am moved.

There he sits, irritating me. Just the sound of pages turning, his cough, are reminders of my disgrace when my sex deceived me and tried to be all of me.

Wretchedly, graph clear, the downward curve races on. This hot confused affair, once a complicated maze in a formal garden, becomes a simple descent. I've worn him down, he scratches in an effort to caress. And what is left for me except occasional wet drunk explosions into emotion more remembered than felt, a phony tenderness as I accept and also resent the ending which is happening.

He tries to beat me back to the original time and chills at my passivity where once I hit back, aroused by any kind of touch, excited by his very fingerprint.

The long season is over, it ends clearly as these November days sharpen and widen in view. Scirocco has left; the sky is blue by day and blue by night. The moon is strong seen, no mist. The mountain is so lucid that it seems smaller.

My humid trance is over.

With terrible logic my sense of nausea has become actual; I vomit in the morning for a whole week till I finally suspect, no accept, that I am pregnant.

Disgust, nausea, irritation, exactly these three; they are my lover.

And I?

Split, torn, sobbing self. An octopus born in the twin month. But my suffering is not divided. There is no doubt in me. I will not carry this man's child.

I see my three children and there is no dilemma. To love them means to hate this foreign object inside me. To conceive a new life one must respect it, and I despise Roberto whose tool I've used, turned against me now as a boomerang.

When the pygmies kill a female elephant the best of the hunters climbs into her womb and then cuts his way out in fierce celebration.

Oh no, the problem is not what to do but how to go about doing it. I want a very brief ritual.

Concertina is not surprised. "I've worried about you for some time, the way you don't eat. But anyway, what do you expect the way you've been carrying on."

"Don't judge me, just help me."

"What about him, what does he say?"

"He doesn't know. I don't want him involved in this."

"You Americans are crazy. He's had his fun with you, why shouldn't he pay for it?"

"Because it's not his fault."

"Well he did it, didn't he?"

"No. I let it happen. Now enough of this. Tell me where to go and then be quiet."

She stares at me; the line between servant and master is thin.

"This is a bad country for women, Signora. There's not a priest who would help you now. They get fat from our sins."

"I know. That's why I'm counting on you."

"But I've no right to help you."

"Do you want to, Concertina?"

"I guess so. I don't know, I'm scared."

"I'm pregnant."

A long silence between us. We're sitting in the kitchen, two women alone. Her simple face looks as sad as any I've ever seen.

She gets up and draws a glass of water, drinks and offers the same glass to me.

"Go and see old Maria, she knows a lot."

Her voice absolves me; the servant has set the master free.

I find Maria's house in the poorest part of town, where there are no streets only vague steps leading down. Steps so narrow, I stumble and feel blind, find the way again, hooked to the last light of afternoon. It will be easier going back.

Rabbit skins nailed to the wall, outside, inside. The yard is gorged with live rabbits, nasty red-eyed animals, much too soft.

She kills them expertly, one neat pull severs the head from the spine. A gash, and the animal is turned inside out.

"One must work for a living," she says, her face so calm and so old that I instantly believe in her.

"Wait till I finish, the butcher is waiting."

In her hands the transition between life and death is so smooth that it's hardly worth watching. I smoke some cigarettes, while she goes on killing, cutting, nailing.

"So you've heard about me?"

"Yes, they say you know the truth."

"Why not, why only talk about good things. I am not a gypsy."

"Will you do it?"

"As you can see, I do everything, just as you want everything."

Black eyes fever into me. My hand in hers is a quivering rabbit. Her vision spurts at me like blood; I am the creature wounded.

"Lie down and let me have a look."

She pushes up her sleeves and goes to the faucet, begins to wash her hands with a green lump of soap. My sigh interrupts her. I lean against a soft wall where the fur of dead animals is nailed in rough squares.

"Don't be afraid, it's only a little pain."

There's no use arguing with a witch, I just leave.

Going up the steps I take a last look down at this wrong place. I need a bigger country.

The first snow has laid a cool glove on the mountain. Soothed, I am able to breathe again, my loneliness is clear fresh air.

That meal is over. Having truly eaten him, I must now rid myself of him. Only a doctor can help me. What difference now another pain, another killing. How true that it becomes easier to live this evil, cutting life. The aborting knife will disinvolve me; a cool clean instrument will erase this last remnant of the humanity that *was* present in those long repeated moments of red forgetting.

French Postcards

Exquise Marquise

Salambo

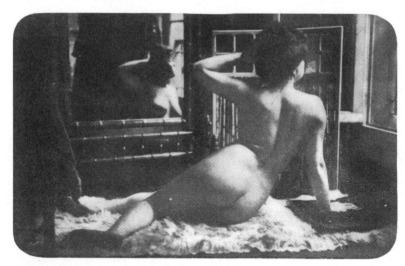

Le Matin

Rêve d'Orient

L'Éponge Indiscrète

Tour de France

Snobinette

Mélodie Perdue

Sortie de Bal

La Cithare Oubliée

La Vie Intérieure

La Nouvelle Vague

Le Petit Confident

Avant l'Extase

Le Premier Soupir

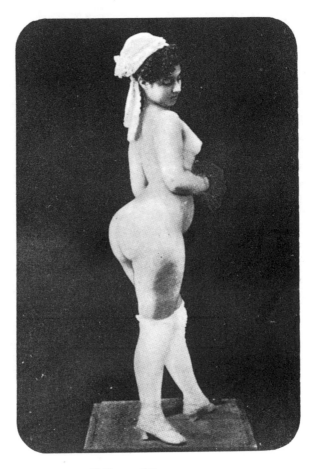

La Promeneuse

IN THE DIRTY PICTURES
by STEPHEN SCHNECK

... always one hideous, gaudy street, sharp as a pimp's necktie and tricky as a marked deck of cards. Renting to dime-a-dance palaces, and sullen poolrooms, and narrow, fly-by-night shops where useless and defective merchandise is forever ON SALE PRICES SLASHED LAST BIG DAY OF BARGAINS GALORE; and switch-blades are displayed next to hand-painted, little living turtles, those ever-popular reptilian souvenirs. There, halfway up the block, two doors down from the sinister, all-nite, fly-specked candy store, is that unlikely establishment: *** AMUSE-MENT CENTER *** FUN TERMINAL *** LAFF RIOT ***

Some riot, but who's laughing? Certainly not the pimply-faced sailor boys, squirming in their crotchtight, bellbottom trousers: squandering their time ashore in these not so amusing centres, where full-grown men play with metal marbles, trying to make the coloured lights on the pinball machines blink and titter and finally tilt.

Who is laughing? Certainly not the shark-eyed, go all nite Negroes; not the penny ante foxes; not the pale, leatherjacket under-age heroes, who hang around . . . hang around. All laughed out in too many Fun

Houses, these amusement centre veterans: shipping clerks by day and killers by night. Scouts of the shooting gallery, where tin duck follows tin duck, forever and ever. Or until the boss goes bankrupt and the electric company shuts off the power. And it's a very rare gunman who sees the bad joke in the inexorable passage of those tin birds, gliding with maddening impunity past the glazed eyes and ready rifles of would-be murderers, blazing away 10 SHOTS 25 c-10 SHOTS at sheet metal phoenixes that fall under the hail of beebee bullets, yet rise again as the treadmill comes around offering a wonderful second chance.

Arcade dreams come true in this maze of pin ball games, shooting galleries, ingenious machines that guess your weight and predict your fortune. And other machines that record your voice . . . a quivering falsetto crying out against your ten-penny fate:

175 lbs.
YOU HAVE A
PLEASING PERSONALITY
*BUT OTHERS MAY NOT
UNDERSTAND*

They certainly don't understand. Else why would we be here among this glumble of inane technology,

219

created for the sole purpose of enticing the hard-won coin from the pocket of the lonely late night loser. Yet, someone must understand . . . though the last bar has long since closed and No Sale signs are rung up all over the city, and nothing waits but the empty furnished room, sad as old love letters, sad as dead flowers, still the neon lights are shining in Playland and one need not be all alone, not yet.

Earth is literally constructed of miraculous caves, curious nooks, treasure groves, holy grottoes, and mysterious crannies. Man, desiring to master his environment, is forever squeezing himself into narrow corners, wiggling in and out of tight spots, peering into every hole, searching for something to keep him amused. Indefatigable, he climbs, he dives, he crosses vast deserts on his belly, hunting for baubles to exchange for other baubles, and creatures more fantastic than himself. Eternally on the trail of the Extraordinary, he is forever speculating on what they have back there . . . and so, innocently following his natural instinct, wanders into the curtained-off alcove at the rear of the Amusement Center, where hum supermachines, the Dirty Picture Machines, busy night and day grinding out man's all-time favourite fairy tale.

GIRLIE FLICKS
ADULTS ONLY

Here, curtains and screens shield shameless fantasy from the pitiless probe of searing neon; substituting bulbs, dim as decency and the local Vice Squad allow, giving off blackish light, strange, pieces of something floating in it. Faint light, not to see by but to dream by.

The machines, nickelodeon-like contraptions, are artfully placed so as to afford a maximum of privacy to the solitary fan who pays his money for a peek at Naked Lady, a short cinematic classic about a naked lady.

TO OPERATE THIS MACHINE
(1) INSERT COIN IN SLOT
(2) LEAN FORWARD TILL NOSE
TOUCHES VIEWING GLASS
(3) OPEN EYES

and watch glamorous model, star-stung beauty, wiggle around without any clothes for six whole reels, only 10 c. a reel. See everything, get nothing. Dirty Machine calling phalluses of the world, arise.

WARNING
DON'T TOUCH THE DIRTY
OLD MACHINE
YOU DON'T KNOW WHO MAY
BE IN IT

and the floodgates of lust, like the

220

box of Pandora, are easy to open but hell to close.

Still, it's only a movie. Isn't it?

Caution . . . there's more to this than meets the burning eye. Pause a moment in the stale air of this passionate backroom where the machines debauch even sound, muffling wild mating cries into the cruel clink of dimes dropping one by one into the coin box. And the piercing flutes of Pan, toned down to a dry flicker of film strips running through an infernal mechanism.

ᵕO Love. A small token illuminates the machine.

SEE

the tall, long-limbed girl, walking sinuously into camera, pulling off her blouse as she comes. A blank face and empty eyes, but expressing herself completely, poignantly, with nothing but her big, bouncing breasts, which jiggle wickedly as she moves still closer. And closer. JUMP CUT TO MED. C.U. OF UPPER TORSO. The ballooning breasts sigh ever so softly as the half-naked girl holds out her arms.

WON'T YOU COME IN
AND LOVE ME

Now answer. The ripe globes pout, and the arms sweep back as she hugs herself. CUT TO LOW ANGLE MED. REAR SHOT of long, sweet legs spreading into mountainous buttocks, split by the deep dark, infamous crease which invites the unclean kiss. The secret face of the dimpled flesh says everything that the mask above tries to conceal.

BOYS
THIS IS ONE MACHINE
THAT KNOWS HOW YOU
LIKE IT

so let your fancies go panting after the saucy creature dangling in front of your nose. Remark how impudent her boiling backside: safe within her prismatic chamber, she bravely, cruelly, flaunts her goodies. Teasing, tantalizing, talented tormentress, watch as she flexes first the right buttock, now the left. Right! Left! Right! CUT TO FULL-LENGTH FRONT VIEW of juicy nude facing the camera, which stares back at her with unblinking eyes of bugs. O so coy, she covers the pubic region with one hand and with the other waves goodbye. Bitter-sweet goodbye.

BLACKOUT
MACHINE OFF

All over. All gone away. Dark, dead, and the hot dream fled till ten cents shall call it back.

The machine giveth, but only for two minutes at a time.

Silent, unspeaking, the men pad

through the labyrinth, passing from machine to machine. Obsessed lovers, seeking their amoratas in opaque windows of impossible dreams. Hardly noticing each other, they drift up and down the aisles, each wrapped in the dense solitude of his own make-believe.

WARNING:
DO NOT TEASE THESE ANIMALS

Still, it is damnably difficult not to peek. Please, just one more peek into another machine and watch that master of distortion, the carelessly handled camera, gasping in suffocating close-up as it successfully invokes the arch-image of concupiscence:

A plump, blonde wanton stretched out on a studio couch. CAMERA DOLLYS IN. All that flesh like bread pudding rising up, engulfing itself, turning into something else. Something like SLOW PAN UP the glossy high heels: up past the deadly spike, the cruel arch, the cunning curve of the heel, and on up into the stratosphere of dark, silky mesh. The promise of burning tongues, unspeakable abandon, somehow conveyed by the line of the seam, ever so slightly askew. Up past giddy frill of a garter for TIGHT SHOT of great bulging thighs, yawning; more

than capable of crushing a longing heart between them. And soiling the soul with flickering, daydreams of feverish girls, dancing forever just a centimetre beyond our reach.

Even God is uneasy in this nervous niche.

Around the machines prowl the ghostly satyrs, shadows in the semi-darkness. Poor raging brutes, dying for a woman, here, in this all-male company. Seeking softness and repose, encountering only more male gristle and bristle and tension unrelieved. Enough to keep any ghost prowling all through the restless night, after some final release. Sniffing around the machines, searching for the way in, the opening through which to explode from unbearable excitation into peace and enduring limpidity.

The hole through which to crawl into the apple-orchard of Paradise, that part of heaven shaped like the lap of a beautiful maid.

To pass there,

FOR BEST RESULTS
REMAIN AT MACHINE
TILL GROSS CORPUS MELTS

and a less solid creature emerges, bloated with dreams, still craving more, sucking on a cyclopian eye that sees nothing but dirty pictures. Thin gruel. Keeps them hungry.

222

LEARN LESSON:
HOW MACHINE TEACHES
US TO LIVE THROUGH
THE EYEBALL

which may be inverted for only ten cents. Inverted eyeballs cause loss of balance and over the edge we go into the stewpot of our own imagination, tasting for one delectable instant the sweet meat of our very own heart. And, in the supreme ecstasy of this fleeting moment, the prayer is answered. We are no longer outside, but indivisible from the machine. Possessed, possessor, we merge with machine.

WE ARE IN THE MOVIES

compliments of the machine. And like the machine, we function simply by running ourselves through ourselves, reel after reel, over and over and over.

Pig-suckers of the demi-world, you've no choice but to move onto the next stall. It seems no choice at all but to wander, hard-pressed, through the compulsive nights, following their erections from machine to machine.

How much can you take?

Answer: How much can I get?

Spend another dime and find out. Possibly this next machine is the one, the only one among all the others, this is the one that will snap your bones and blow out all the connections.

Step up. Drop your dime into the slot, and for once

SOMETHING IS GOING
TO HAPPEN
SOMETHING IS GOING
TO FLASH

on the viewing screen.

Gorgeous beast greets you with a toss of her hindquarters, broad as a brood-mare's; then turns the other cheek to face you, open, simple, just a luscious, uncomplicated country girl with a petrified leer. Try not to find something familiar about this heavyrumped, walleyed milkmaid, climbing out of her clothes, just on the other side of the viewing screen. Wheat-coloured hair pulled back into a single, thick braid, falling all the way down her naked, rolling back Awkward, tender. Mincing about in a droll parody of *la grande dame* at her toilet: playing the narcissistic charmer, indulging herself in the intimacy of her own boudoir. Some strange boudoir . . . where all the furniture is rented by the hour, right down to the very last piece, including Sweet Alice herself. That doesn't matter. Wherever it came from, just so long as it's there, waiting for you in the machine; the bud of flesh swelling up through the inevitable black silk stockings, straining the elastic of her unlikely garterbelt till it's taut as leather and binding as the harness of a fantasy, some half-forgotten daydream of this ripe wench, hitched to the plough, dragging the demonic viewer on through fields of fever. Driving her on, with his hands frantically playing in his pockets, and his breath so hot it steams the viewing glass.

IS SHE THE ONE?

If not, nothing for it but to move down the line, press against the next machine. See them all, dime by dime. See, the tall and the short, the she-goats as well as the cooing doves. If this one doesn't **make** you happy, the next one surely will. So try your luck, again and again. There's little enough to be lost in this motorized grabbag of buttock and celluloid thigh.

Even so, nobody's **dimes** last for ever, and there's still a long, terrible night to kill.

A very long night for the boys who have no girls.

"O those creeps," shrug the Ladies of the Real World, turning away from the naked need in the unhealthy faces of the creeps of the earth.

Ugly as warthogs and smelly as public toilets, the lads with no place to go and nobody to go there with them line up for the dirty picture machines, glad to take whatever they can get.

Ancient perverts with sad, muddy eyes rub shoulders, and more, with acne-spattered youngsters, bright sprouts erupting in their own juices. Fathers and sons, all lean together while the machine mutters the only invitation they're likely to hear, the timid whisper of the mouse inside. The poor little mouse that never stops gnawing, never stops whispering. Here in the dim, machine-crowded grotto, one cannot help but overhear the queer, starving, repulsive little rodent, sighing into the viewer,

SEE, SEE
SEE HOW BEAUTIFUL
THE NAKED LADY
LOVES
YOU

and bits of wadded-up Kleenex, scattered around the base of the machines, like pale offerings around a shrine. Pungently scented evidence of auto-erotic activity. Just passion spilled out on the butt-littered floor. Passion that had to be given . . . though nobody wanted it. Now transformed into puddles for others to step over.

So much love going to waste at ten cents a pound, and no takers except the machine. No nothing but

224

make-believe sweethearts who come out when you drop the coin and press the button that starts them shaking that thing, offering the plump rump, kindling impossible desire in the fierce, too often repulsed, yearning loins of the Despised. Creeps. The boys who get to come only in their dreams, in front of the dirty picture machine. And be he less than a squirming maggot.

THIS MACHINE GUARANTEED
*NOT TO TURN AWAY
FROM ANYONE*

and all he needs is a dime in his paw. One sweaty dime is all it takes to make the machine light up, and bring on the obliging, undressed madonnas who give themselves with equal fervour to toad and tiger alike, Come, reject, nosepicker, crotch-scratcher, chewed up, spat out, wormy little fellow; the lewd lady will strip for you too. Whoever you . are.

MACHINE DEAF, DUMB
NEVER TELLS SECRETS

and no end to mysteries.

Where do they come from, these marvellous girls, depraved nymphs providing so much vile pleasure? Where do they come from, and where O where do they go? After the last foot of film has been exposed, and the anonymous cameraman packs his equipment, while his cigar-chewing assistant takes down the floodlights, do you, Beauty, dress hurriedly behind a shaky screen? And notice the chill now that the hot lights are off? Curse a run that suddenly appeared in the stockings you bought only that morning?

How close we all are to each other.

Unknown fiend trembling in front of this dirty picture machine, watching some brazen young lovely, anxious for money, knowing she has to start somewhere, anywhere: so it might as well be waving her bosom in a rented studio, two thousand miles away, six months ago.

And still these two, separated from each other on every level, every dimension, surmount all barriers and manage to come together, bisecting each other's life line on that broad and final plane, where all such lines meet, in that turbid alcove at the rear of the arcade.

Boys and girls, could it be.

ALL TOGETHER
*IN THE DIRTY PICTURE
MACHINE*

One trapped inside, the other languishing outside; embracing through a glass partition, in the flickering light of dreams that last just long enough to make you want more. Till

BLACKOUT

I WORSHIP PAPERCLIPS
by KAJA

Please, nobody take from me these
unsolved idiosyncracies of my
nature.
Let me alone until I settle.

I am a house of most fantastic
structure—a paperclip for the
window.
The steps are staple guns—my
clothes are rubber bands!
My days are clothespins!
I keep a firing squad of empty jars
and little cardboard boxes.

I am obsessed with paperclips.
Do not separate me from my
obsession.
My life needs paperclips!
The hours will not hold the
minutes.
My days get lost from their weeks.

I leap from Saturn to Mercury
without having the least idea what
I'm doing.
You can understand how this loose
space travel is distracting.

If I could just settle down—one
hour! One place!
Impossible!
The clock keeps changing. As soon
as you get adjusted to 9.00 A.M.,
it's Noon!

I have a lot of trouble with the
hours in the day.

I don't really have 24 of them. The
taxes that I have to pay tonight
leave me really very little income.
I thought I had 16 hours to spend
just like I wanted, like Van
Gogh did.
There are not 16 hours that I can
call my own:

The sizes of the hours. Look,
there are two of them small as
green peas, and another like a
strawberry.
Suddenly there's one: whole as a
watermelon! How to weight
these hours?
they won't make a dozen!

Paperclips! I need paperclips to
hold my hours!

I've never had much feeling for
zippers or buttons.
Paste and rubber cement leave me
cold.
I like Scotch Tape for its tickle.
Rubber bands give me a sense of
power, because I can use them to
tie up my hair.

When it comes to drawers and
shelves and cupboards,
I have such a profound respect for
them, that I pile my file-folders
on the floor.

Rooms are a little more my speed.
I look for hours in doorways; I
think doorways are sacred.
I paint them blue.

226

I think a flat sheet of paper
is more powerful than an envelope.

I know I should be thinking dogs,
not paperclips . . .
Thinking blankets, birds, milk,
fruit and vegetables.
I dream salads and cafeterias; I
don't dream Paperclips.
I dream Dogs, Wounds, Death,
Flying Lessons in a white house,
I don't dream Paperclips.

Fifteen years ago some Oranges
and Radishes came to get me, but
I wouldn't listen; I thought it was
just my imagination.

Why go off the deep end?

If I could have believed the
Radishes, if I could have believed
the green girl walking down the
street with Hair that followed in
her wake like waves after a ship
transforming the coastline,
If I could have believed what I
imagined then, (how her hair
flowed like water into all the dead
doorways, how the tide of her hair
rose like blessing purifying every
substance touched) I wouldn't have
needed to worship Paperclips.

How could I believe in Oranges?
Could I assume these ridiculous
radishes in place of street lamps
weren't just making fun of me?
Who could have told me Christ
was an Orange, how much sooner

should I have taken a Saviour . . .
the vision with green hair,

had she only some sainted name I
should have been devout rather
than separate.

I am the fate of visionaries to
whom the symbols of the universe
have not be educated to come
traditionally.

The Paperclip!
Oh he is warped and twisted, he
shines and twists like a musical
instrument he shouts at me
methodically:

PAPERCLIPS! RADISHES!

When I won't listen, to make his
story louder, He comes in the
Thousand Forms and names of
fear,

comes working my crevices, the
sculpture of my absences:

PAPERCLIP!

THE CONTEST
by JONATHAN KOZOL

Ten days after his thirteenth birthday:

An automobile turns out of the asphalt road, pursues two miles of granite and black hill to the tall walls that hem the sacred grove. His father (Aaron Schreiber, B.S. Harvard: Harvard M.D.) discovers the gate to Christ's Chapel, and enters in. As it happens, he has discovered the wrong entrance— not the Main Gate but the Service Gate. And yet: what matter, the manner if one arrives in the right place?

The right place is the Headmaster's Study. David will follow his father into the office of Horton Rogers, Latin Master and Headmaster of the school. Aaron is known to Rogers in several ways. One: before David's grandmother could read or speak English, Aaron had been journeying each day from the black tenement into the subway tunnel, within the narrow channel to the last stop, there emerging to do commerce as he might amid the swift aristocrats of Harvard: while Rogers mildly progressed across the court for breakfast among his peers in the College Union. At least one world separated the precise Anglican from the driving insurgent of Judengasse and Judendorf, and yet (specifically) Rogers must accept this fact: they are *classmates*. Thus in insidious ways did Harvard College desecrate the tasteful preference of its scholars, disrupting (but not overthrowing) a frail Establishment. Once again, much later, Rogers had reason (which must be need) to traverse a personal path with David's father: Rogers' sister had a dangerous miscarriage. Inquiries were made into the matter of specialists and, with something between fascination and outrage, he discovered that the best man in the field was Dr. Schreiber. So Aaron took the case, handled it well, got the Headmaster's sister past her demon, and earned his reluctant (if not the less fullhearted) admiration.

In later years, when he married and had children, and an obstetrician was demanded in the wee hours, Rogers addressed himself as a matter of course to Aaron, became in some qualified sense fond of the man, and finally made the generous mistake of suggesting that he send his son to be groomed at Christ's Chapel.

The difference between David's home in Padan Aram and the Episcopal Gothic halls of Christ's Chapel Meadows was not less great than the six-week steerage journey that separated the Warsaw ghetto of Hagar's youth from the house in Louisberg Square where Horton Rogers' mother had preened and primped for the December Cotillion of 1880. It took more than one man or one generation to bridge that gap; but two men and two generations could do it. Hagar had made it from Warsaw to Boston Light; Aaron had made it from Boston to Harvard Yard; in more than the journeyman's sense David would be expected to make it to the top of Beacon Hill.

And as he thought back to that morning in the Headmaster's Study, and pictured his father (expendable intermediary) fulfilling the one rôle that sociology allotted him, David could not permit a distressing whimsy from painting the following scene; his father on his knees in the mud beneath the window of an English abbey; a boy of thirteen or fourteen putting one foot on his father's back then both feet in order to lift himself up to the window-level. Inside the window: a dark-panelled room, a graceful man in a rust-coloured jacket and dark trousers, standing before a bookcase. The man turns as David's face appears in the window. He smiles and beckons David to come in. As David climbs down into the room, dusting off his jacket and new trousers, the man sets his pipe in a pewter ashtray and comes forward. He speaks with handsome curiosity—comely restraint. "How'd you manage it, young fellow?"

With proper shyness, David points out the window: "My father —he's down there in the mud; I climbed in on his back."

The man in the rust-coloured jacket breaks into appreciative laughter: "Good show, young fellow! Good show!"

"Is it all right for him to stay out there?" David says. "Will anyone mind?"

The schoolmaster chuckles a bit, then says in a generous manner: "No, no, let him stay. Nobody will see him." After a moment's pause, he adds: "Of course you won't be using that entrance any longer; from now on you can come in the regular way."

"Oh thank you sir," says David.

Then, thinking again of the clever fellow's ingenuity, the master comes forward and pats David twice on the shoulder. He repeats, in a genial and approving manner: "Darn good show, David Schreiber! We can use you, David Schreiber!"

Borden Rogers was the Headmaster's son; he was not blond-haired and blue-eyed but he carried off his brown hair and brown eyes more successfully than David

Schreiber did. Peter Stanton's father was also a master at Christ's Chapel. Barker and Barnett were children of Harvard deans. Henry Cutter's father was a professor at the Medical School. Bucky Clapp's father was headmaster of a girl's school called Miss Brattle's Country Day. All in all, David could see that the boys in his class at Christ's Chapel belonged to a closely wrought unity of blood, money, and values, although (even at that age) he could see that the latter two were already on the wane; and the first and vital element would be prey within a decade's time to the gradual adulteration of such alien fluid as his own.

About one thing there was no debate in David's heart: moral qualms did not enter the field. He felt himself a wholly free agent within the reasonable bounds of Christ's Chapel Meadows. His father had made the mistake or generous sacrifice of placing him in a world of rarified air where he himself was unable to survive; his penalty would be that of all self-effacing parents: David's inward (later, outward) self would acclimate its basic characteristics to function on a new and different level. And if he should never come back, in any genuine sense, to the world his mother and father still inhabited, it would not be wholly a matter of choice with him, not just the snobbish volition of a thankless child, but rather perhaps a process of natural law: the working-out of an easy postulate: that the son could no longer breathe the old kind of air, any more than his father would be able to breathe the new.

Crandall Brooks goes around the class. He is stern, one-browed, glass-jawed: his eyes are the clear blue heirlooms of a handsome Aryan line.

"Barker?"

"Here, sir: High Church."

"Barnett?"

"Here, sir: High Church."

"Clapp?"

"Yes, sir: High Church."

"Cutter?"

"Sir, Presbyterian!"

Loud guffaws and cheekpops; Fat Jellicoe, sitting behind Cutter, kicks mercilessly at his desk chair: bam! bam! bam! while sundry soprano boy-voices cry out: "He's a nigger! Cutter's black! Poor Cutter! Cutter's blackassed!"

Crandall Brooks blinks his blue heirlooms, slowly sensing (albeit in an un-self-reproaching fashion) that he might have made a mistake. But Cutter's holding up all right. A good fellow. Lots of pluck. On with the game. If you're in the club you've got to obey the rules. If you don't like the rules, you didn't have to join.

"Duncan?"

"Endicott?"

"Frost?"

"High Church."

"Sir: High Church!"

"Sir: Lutheran."

"Grantley?"

"Harkness?"

"Henley?"

"Hodges?"

"High Church!"

"High Church!"

"High Church!"

"High Church!"

The four voices come from the same back row. Crandall smiles at something as he jots down his figures on the back of an envelope.

"Ireland?"

"Jaspers?"

"Jellicoe?"

Fat Jellicoe prepares for the big joke; he looks around at Barker and Stanton and nods; they poke each other in the ribs and catch Bucky Clapp's attention: the class pokes and jabs; the signal ripples about the room.

Timmy Ireland answers his name: "Sir: I'm a Lutheran."

Skeleton-tall Jaspers answers his name: "Sir: Anglican!"

The class titters with laughter; everyone is ready for the joke.

Fat Jellicoe sits forward in his chair. He cocks his pink face innocently up at the master: "Sir: I'm a little Jewish boy."

The class explodes into anticipated laughter, even though the reason for it does not seem so great now as before: it was not such a good joke after all.

Crandall Brooks is not completely stupid. He realizes at last the error he has made; he is ready to concede his carelessness. Next year, he will not make the same mistake. How then to get through the game without causing any more needless pity upon a brow in the second row. Cleverness serves the crisis. The master knows what to do.

"Johnson?"

"High Church!"

"Lawrence?"

"High Church!"

"Lowell?"

"Sir, High Church!"

"Morley?"

"Newbegin?"

"Parker?"

"Strethers?"

"Truslow?"

Lobotomy of the mind: a term recurrent in David's thoughts. The cold steel blade of the knife . . .

The night at Black Quarry grew chill with the imminence of autumn's first dawn. In uneven sleep before the morning David sweated rapidly a sick chill sweat. His elbows were pressed to his sides, his hands drawn up beneath his chest. He dreamed a rapacious series of meaningless ordeals: the chewing, biting, sucking of a hard rubbery substance: the passage in blanched moonglare over an etherous terrain: The formulation of phrases, their rearrangement . . .

The stench in the room was an old thing: the reek of many muscular young men exuding perspiration as the afternoon died its winter death. He could see the room clearly: the large rubberized mat, the stuffed weights and pulleys against the far wall, the exercising tables on the side, the benches for the parents and the teams, the wooden stools for the referee and timer; beyond it all, the frosted windows, the darkness of the encroaching night, and the distant stone tower of Christ's Chapel Hall.

He was trying to decide the year. It must have been his last winter. He was wrestling one-thirty-two; he was limbering up his muscles. He was doing exercises. One! and two and one! and two. The coach (a little stunted man: Ben Baker, the Bio Master) came up to him and asked how the ankle felt. "The ankle is good, sir." "She's okay, is she?" "Yes, sir." The coach

scrutinized him carefully, then patted him on the back: "Good stuff, Schreiber! Good stuff! You're a good man!" "Thank you, sir." "Schreiber, I want you to suck a lemon: when the acid gets on your tongue it turns to sugar: $H_2O + CO_2$ yields H_2CO_3." "Yes, Sir! Thank you, sir!" "Good going, boy!" David sucked at the lemon-rind and began hopping from foot to foot. One! and two and one! and two. He had not noticed the large audience before; all the parents were coming for the match; all the girls from Miss Brattle's Country Day; some girls came all the way from Virginia. Everyone came. David limbered up: he loosened his muscles: he sucked his lemon. The Headmaster came across the mat: "How are we going to do, boy?" "We're going to win, sir." Horton smiled proudly: "Good show, Schreiber. You're a good man." Then, putting his arm over David's shoulder, he whispered, "You know, just between you and me, Schreiber, I've never regretted letting you in."

David sat on the bench in his black tights. He watched the Hebrew boys practising on the other side of the mat. The School for the Hebrew Blind produced the best wrestlers in the League—something about not being able to see improved muscle-tone: tensile strength and visceral acuity correlated: he didn't entirely understand it. Ben Baker had explained it once.

David bit his lower lip as he tried to determine which of the blind wrestlers was his man. They all looked awfully big. He didn't see a single one that could have made one-thirty-two. They always went easy on the weights of the blind; it didn't seem fair to David. A game was a game. If you joined the team you had to obey the rules. If you didn't like the rules you didn't have to join. Like putting out your hand first so the blind man could find you. Was that sort of thing really necessary?

Suddenly the referee got up in the middle of the mat, holding his stool. He announced the next match but he did not give the names. David was bothered by this. When you are in the running, you want all your names down on the board. Otherwise you don't know where you are. But then David realized they were waiting for *him;* they were calling out *his* name. His presence was desired at the centre of the mat.

The whistle was blown three times. The referee ran to the side of the mat and sat on his little stool. David moved forward stealthily, his head and shoulders low, knees bent, weight forward. He moved carefully, swinging his arms cleverly, turning his head from side to side. He imagined the muscularity of his calves.

As the fellow approached him, David noticed that his arms and shoulders were thickly knotted with muscles; there was a dark growth of hair upon his chest; his head was heavy and stumplike at the end of a short solid neck. He began dangling his arms in David's direction. David reached out one hand and offered it to the blind man; he felt a desperate fist clutch his wrist.

The first informal give and take were over. Now they were in it for good. The strong hand of his opponent clamped inexorably on the back of David's neck. One of his own hands pressed on the back of the blind man's neck. Their shoulders and heads remained low as they sprang and lunged with a bouncing rhythm back and forth across the mat. The point at this stage was to conserve your strength. "Conserve your strength, Schreiber," the coach would say, the same way he said, "Suck a lemon, Schreiber," or "Keep your eyes on your man, Schreiber." But David could not keep his eyes on his man; his head was being pressed down. The hand of the blind man was too strong to resist. David wondered why his opponent would not let him see his face: as if he were ashamed of something, as if he were embarrassed at being blind.

Then David began to notice something extremely unpleasant. The Hebrew man was sweating profusely; and his sweat exuded the foulest odour that David had ever smelled. "Why don't they ever wash?" he wondered. And the more he thought about it the more furious he became. It seemed unbelievable that any man could smell so foul; even in the crowded sweat-bathed wrestling-room the odour of David's opponent stood out unmistakably from all the other smells. The girls from Miss Brattle's School drew scented handkerchiefs up to their noses. And their eyes spoke words of unimaginable distress. Their boyfriends on the team caught the silent message and glared back at them with brave offers in the set of their jaws.

At that moment his opponent made a wild lunge for David's knees, wrapped his arms about them, and threw him over. The next thing David knew, he was being strangled and pressed down upon the mat by a Three-Quarter-Nelson. He struggled to keep his shoulders from meeting the mat. Meanwhile a startling thought occurred to him, something for which he suffered untold regrets: he had wrestled this man before! He knew it as certainly as he knew he was about to be pinned. That smell, those heavy shoulders, that hairy chest, the dark hue of the skin—all these things struck home with David: they were all somehow familiar to his inmost memory. He was certain that he had wrestled with this man before, and not just once, but many times. There had been a whole history of matches. Where was it? And when?

But now there was no time for thought. It was too late for that. David was on the verge of being pinned. If he lost this round, he lost the match; if he lost the match, he lost all. He sensed the peculiar importance of the match—something greater than anyone else in the room could have guessed. The boys on the bench and the visitors began to cheer for David:

Give him a Ra!
Ra! Ra! Ra!
Give him a Ra!
Ra! Ra! Ra!
Give him a Ra!

It was good to know that they were with him. But it would not help much so long as his man held him in that Nelson. All at once, the blind fellow switched his body position and altered his hold: he reached down between David's legs

234

to get him in a Full-Body-Press. The hand that caught him between the legs was frenetic and rapacious; it clutched at his groin. It was only at that moment that David realized his mistake: he no longer had on his supporter! He tried to think where he could have lost it; it must have fallen off while he was limbering up. But then he noticed an odd coincidence: his opponent was not wearing one either. Perhaps the Hebrew coach, seeing the plight of the Christ's Chapel boy, decided it would only be fair sport to even the scales, and ordered his own man to go naked into the mat. (That would be good show, David thought.)

At about the same moment, the girls on the bench noticed the same thing: *that the two wrestlers were naked.* They had nothing on their bodies: no wrestling-tights, no jerseys, no supporters. David did not like the feeling of the blind man's body crawling and stretching all over his own with that greasy oil-slick. Now at least he knew what the smell had been: it was Oil of Pomegranate. The Hebrew wrestlers always rubbed it over their bodies. Christ's Chapel used Wintergreen ointment, which was traditional in the league.

When he realized that his man was ready to burst his testicles within his fist. David became doubly frightened. Moreover, something about the finger-action on his penis had caused a considerable erection. It was impossible to conceal, even though the man was lying on top of it. David shuddered to imagine the girls in the audience. He could just bet this was the last match Bucky's father would let the Brattle girls attend! At that moment, while their two bodies were almost entirely contiguous on the mat, David heard his opponent make strange spluttering sounds through his nose; then he realized that the poor fellow was trying to talk:

"Shhh! Psssst! Da-da-da . . ."

He felt awfully sorry for the fellow. It was surely a pitiful business. But what was his horror when he opened his eyes at last! (How long had he kept them closed? Had anyone seen?) What was his horror when he looked at last upon that apelike face and saw those bulging eyeballs rolling in enormous sockets beneath the receding forehead. There was an anthropoid face if he ever saw one! And where else had he seen it—but . . .

He shuddered with recognition! He trembled and felt an enormous desire to be sick. That face! That hateful face! That detestable semitic face! Those yellowed teeth! That unmistakable nose! That dark and sallow skin! Where could there be two like that in the world? He felt a sudden pressing and squeezing at his testicles, as though to get his attention. Then these words finally spluttered forth, very jerkily, directly into his ear (along with a great deal of saliva):

"They wouldn't let me in unless I did it. I'm sorry, son, if I've embarrassed you; I don't want to retard your career; but I had to see you, and they only let blind men on the team. So I did it. I did it with a fire-poker. But, don't worry! I can still see. See!" (He blinked one white-clouded eye feverishly.) "They don't know it but I have a cataract—I can still see through that. I can see you beautifully and you look good to me. It's a fine sight for an old father's eyes to know his boy is still in there pitching."

David felt an irresistible wave of repulsion surge through him. Scrutinizing the hideous face in front of him, he wanted to vomit. "But— you're so ugly!" he said. And then he asked: "Do you realize how you have humiliated me? What this means in terms of years wasted, progress retarded?"

"I'm sorry, son." And tears of a thick whitish substance oozed from the corners of the old man's eyes. "You are the dearest thing there is to me in the world, and I only wanted to have a little look at you. Just to see your face: your fine clean face. You are incorruptible, my son. Incorruptible. You are clean inside and out: a gentleman through and through. I'm proud of you, my boy. I don't even need your love as a reward. Hate me if you wish. Any emotion will do as well: just to know you are thinking of me."

David looked into his father's oozing cataract: "This is the worst moment of my life. I have hated you, but never so much as at this instant."

"That's all right, boy. That's all right!" (Squeezing at the testicles.) "Is there anything I can do to make it up to you? Just name it and I'll do it."

Fury burned in David's eyes. "Yes," he said at last, "you can let me loose so I won't be beaten. That's what you can do, if you're any father at all."

"Am I a father or aren't I?" said his opponent. "Just watch this!" And suddenly the old man wrenched his arm out from between David's thighs, and seemed to have injured his wrist. He examined it for a moment, and in that split second David was up and on him. He wasted no time. To the redoubled cheers of his team-mates and their girls, David grabbed the blind man's weak arm and twisted it behind his back, pulling it out on the other side of his shoulder. Then he dug his knees into the trapped man's stomach, and locked his legs down on the mat by manipulating the arches and insteps of his own feet. Now he had him where he wanted him. He smiled hideously and triumphantly: this was one chance of revenge in a million: he would be a fool to pass it by! Gouging his victim's intestines with his bony knee, David leaned forward over the face whose every detail he so unflinchingly despised. He knew what had to be done. First giving a sharp crack to the wounded arm to make sure the ligaments were split, David splayed out his own two longest fingers (on his left hand; he was the only lefty in his family) and gloated over the nasty sties that the poor fellow thought to pass off for eyeballs.

"What are you going to do, my boy?" said the old man in a gentle loving voice that quivered with only the slightest cackle of fear.

"I am going to dig out the last streams of light in your eyes," David said. "That's what I'm going to do."

"Oh please, son! Please don't do that. Then I shan't be able to see

you even a bit. And all my life's work shall have been in vain. I shan't even have the blessed joy of seeing you triumph over all the world."

"That's the whole idea, old man. Take a good look if you want. It's the last look you'll ever have."

"It's a beautiful face, son. A fine courageous countenance. Handsome through and through. You will do great things, boy. I will not be here to see them, but you will do great things."

"You'll be here," said David. "You just won't see them." And he laughed malignantly. He splayed out his two nail-sharp fingers, and tested their length. Catching the spirit of the thing, the bench and the visitors began to cheer:

Pluck out his eyes!

Ra Ra Ra!

Pluck out his eyes!

Ra Ra Ra!

Meanwhile the other bench, realizing their man needed support, began to chant a Hebrew cheer:

Yisgaddal, Yisgaddash!

Yisborach, V'yishtabbach!

V'yispoar, V'yisromam!

V'yisnasseh, V'yishaddor!

V'yisalleh, V'yishallol!

O-men! O-men! O-men!

"Prayers won't help you now, poor fellow," thought David with a wince of pity. (Supposing he were down there and somebody were about to pluck out his eyes?) But he quickly banished such reservations from his mind. There was no time for pity now. That should have been thought of long ago. He could have kicked himself for forgetting, but now it was too late. *I am about my father's work,* he thought. If anyone asked about it, that is what he would say: *his father's work!* (He laughed at the very thought of it!) Now the cheering reached a deafening peak; the voices of all the Brattle girls were with him:

Ra Ra Ra!

Pluck out his eyes!

Ra Ra Ra!

He heard the coach saying, "Keep your eyes on your man, Schreiber! Muscle tone correlated with visceral acuity. Go to it, Schreiber!" He waited no longer but bore down now upon his object: his nails pierced the first glassy level of the cornea, digging into the gelatinous area where the pigments and optic nerves were twisted about. As he scraped at the bottoms of the eyeballs, he could feel, specifically, the pupils, the irises, the tear-ducts, the tear-glands. The cataract itself was neither more nor less than an obnoxious white creamlike substance with brown tinges as when curd begins to oxidize. He scraped it all up in the ends of his nails.

Meanwhile the Hebrew boys kept cheering their man:

Yisgaddal! Yisgaddash!

O-men! O-men!

They certainly do have pluck, thought David. He could tell that the audience thought so too. As when in the ball-park a fellow misses a catch but leaps several feet in the air in the effort, wrenching his knee, a murmur of assent and approval begins to rise in the stands—so now the visitors' and homebenches alike began to ripple with the natural sympathy and pity which are aroused in all human hearts at the sight of human pain. Soon the entire room was bursting with applause and rocking to the chant that came from all sides of the mat:

Good for the Jew! He's not dead!

Good for the Jew!

He's not dead!

David found himself forgotten in the surge of applause for the beaten man. He heard Horton Rogers saying to one of the masters: "I'm sure I've seen that man before. I wonder if he's the fellow who begs in the Boston Gardens during the Ice Capades?" David was jealous of the beaten man. He felt it was a hollow victory. But wasn't it always like that? Hadn't he always been cheated? And, in that instant, a tremendous fury began to surge in David's heart. He knew what he would have to do. All at once, amidst startled cries from both sides of the mat, David began to vomit unrelentingly upon the bleeding face of his victim; the vomit dripped and spewed also on his own chest and stomach and testicles. He vomited convulsively for several seconds; then, when the solid substance was exhausted, he continued an erratic and uncontrollable retching for several minutes more. The voices of the people in the room became less and less important: they ceased to qualify. And, as they lost significance, they also lost volume: they became dimmer and dimmer, more and more blurred. Waves of nauseous fatigue heaved David to and fro on the mat. He felt hot and cold chills burning and numbing his skin; his shoulders and back seemed very cold. He tried to pull the cover up over his waist, but it would not come; something was holding it back: a weight of some sort. It was caught. He trembled frantically and began to shiver. His forehead was hot with fever; his eyes felt heavy. He was afraid he would vomit again but he had not had anything more to eat. All he could do was retch. He felt the tearing start in again on his stomach. Suddenly, in infantile panic, he sat up in bed and gasped for breath. He did not begin to retch a second time but instead felt hot tears moving over his cheeks, and his chest was heaving with sobs.

PUBLISHER'S AFTERWORD

The Olympia Press, founded in Paris in 1953 by Maurice Girodias, has played a vital role in the movement towards free expression in art and literature. Its major creation, The Traveller's Companion Series, has included first editions in English of *Lolita* and *The Ginger Man,* Jean Genet's *Thief's Journal* and *Our Lady of the Flowers,* de Sade's novels, William Burroughs' *Naked Lunch,* Samuel Beckett's *Watt* and *Molloy,* some of Henry Miller's major works and, among many other discoveries, the unique and frivolous *Candy.*

Now that the great battle against literary censorship has been nearly completely won in Great Britain and in the United States, The Traveller's Companion Series enters a new phase of its existence, and emerges at last from a long exile. From now on, it will be published simultaneously in London and New York with the same famous green cover, and under the editorship of Maurice Girodias. A Scandinavian multi-lingual Traveller's Companion is already in existence, and the Series will soon expand to other languages and other countries, making it a unique enterprise in the history of publishing, and multiplying the chances it can offer to unknown authors.

An essential task of the new Traveller's Companion Series will, naturally, be as ever to discover new talents. Manuscripts are welcome, and should be sent to the editorial headquarters: The Olympia Press, 7 rue Saint-Séverin, Paris 5, France. No responsibility can be accepted for manuscripts submitted and authors are advised to retain a carbon or photostat in each case.

Above all, the ambition of the new Traveller's Companion Series is to become the image of the newly-won liberties: the right for everyone to think, to write and to read freely—for pleasure alone.